*In the forest in the Bertam valley, Cameron Highlands, Malaya
(4,700 feet altitude)*

PLANT LIFE IN MALAYA

PLANT LIFE IN MALAYA

R. E. HOLTTUM

M.A., Sc.D. (Cantab.)
Formerly Professor of Botany,
University of Singapore

LONGMAN

LONGMAN GROUP LIMITED
London

LONGMAN MALAYSIA SDN BERHAD
44 Jalan Ampang, Kuala Lumpur

*Associated companies, branches and representatives
throughout the world*

First published 1954
New impressions 1957, 1961, 1964
First Paperback Edition *1969

SBN 582 69445 0

Printed in Hong Kong by
The Hong Kong Printing Press Ltd.

CONTENTS

ACKNOWLEDGMENTS

For permission to copy from drawings the publishers are indebted to the following: the Editor of the *Malayan Nature Journal* and Mr. M. R. Henderson for Figs. 43a^2 and 47d; the Editor of *De Tropische Natuur*, 1931 and 1933, for Figs. 44c and 46a; and the Royal Horticultural Society for Figs. 47e and 47e^1 from the *Botanical Magazine*, vol. 56, plate 7719.

NOTE

The drawings in this book have been made by Miss Leong Hong Tim and Mr. Juraimi bin Samsuri under the supervision of the author, and are copyright by the publishers.

NOTE ON SECOND IMPRESSION

Various small errors have been corrected in this impression. I am grateful to Mr. P. R. Wycherley of the Rubber Research Institute of Malaya for the information that Hevea trees are (at least in part) insect-pollinated in Malaya, and an appropriate correction is therefore made on p. 80.

A reviewer has said that in view of the preponderance of trees among Malayan plants, more space should have been devoted to them. I hope however that readers in Malaya are already acquainted with Mr. Corner's excellent and comprehensive *Wayside Trees of Malaya* (quoted on p. 6; published by the Government Printer, Singapore), and would commend it to readers in other countries who wish to know more about this important aspect of plant life in Malaya.

R. E. H.

PREFACE

Plant life in Malaya is a very complex subject. It is complex in many ways, partly because there are so many kinds of plants, partly because of the great diversity of form and structure among those plants, and partly because the peculiar Malayan climate evokes different kinds of response from different plants; and in all these aspects of plant life in Malaya our knowledge is at present very imperfect, as compared with knowledge of plants in temperate regions.

The task of presenting an introduction to this complex subject therefore involves choice from an enormous field of knowledge, and some of the statements are bound to be tentative. No two people would set about the task in the same way, and no single person has an intimate acquaintance with the whole subject. The choice of material here presented necessarily reflects my own personal interests, and gives emphasis to those plants of which I have special knowledge. I have, however, attempted to cover as wide a field as possible, and I hope that the result is not seriously unbalanced. There is clearly scope for other books on similar lines to this one, elaborating those aspects of the subject which are here omitted or briefly mentioned.

I hope this book may be useful to a variety of people. It is intended primarily for the Malayan resident who wishes to begin a study of Malayan plants. It includes the kind of information about plants which I think should be taught in Malayan schools, and I hope it will be useful to teachers who have had no special botanical training; it should also be useful to students in their last year at school and their first year at the university.

Most of the plants mentioned in the book are common, and I hope that the local reader will look for those plants and examine them as he reads. Uncommon plants are only mentioned where they are of especial interest (e.g. Rafflesia). As it is impossible to describe all plants in detail, the book is illustrated with drawings to help readers to recognize the plants, and also to indicate details of interest. I hope also that these drawings will help readers outside Malaya, who cannot go to the plants themselves. Almost all the drawings have been made from living plants. A few have been made from dried specimens, and a few have been copied or adapted from other books, or from the collection of drawings in the Botanic Gardens, Singapore. The drawings in figures 4 to 14 are by Mr. Juraimi bin Samsuri, artist at the Botanic Gardens. The rest are all the work of Miss Leong Hong Tim, and I wish especially to thank her for the time and skill and critical thought she has devoted to them.

I have beer studying plant life in Malaya for thirty years. During that period I have acquired knowledge in many ways, much of it from other people and from books. The information here presented therefore comes from many sources, and I have not attempted to indicate those sources. I would like, however, to express my indebtedness to my botanical colleagues, both in Malaya and in other parts of the world, from whom I have learned much; and to the many people who have called my attention to particular plants, thereby enlarging the scope of my thought and knowledge.

Singapore, *January* 1953   R. E. HOLTTUM

CHAPTER ONE

EVERGREEN MALAYA

MALAYA has no cool season, and (except in the extreme north) very slight dry seasons. In most parts of the country, rain falls throughout the year. As a result, Malaya is a green country. The forest is evergreen, and the countryside is mainly evergreen, apart from rice-fields at harvest, and apart from the seasonal flowering of a few kinds of deciduous trees (mostly not native) in some places. But comprising this ever-present greenness are an enormous number of different kinds of plants, behaving in many different kinds of ways.

An evergreen tree is one that is always covered with leaves. That is, the old leaves fall after the new ones have grown. How long after? How often do new leaves grow? In most cases, we do not know the answer to these questions, and different trees certainly give us many different answers.

One of the slowest-growing trees is a Mangosteen. In Singapore, Mangosteen trees are uniformly covered with their dark green glossy leaves, except for a short period once or twice a year when some (rarely all) of the branches produce new leafy twigs. The new leaves are light green for a short period, but soon acquire a dark colour like the rest. I do not know of any observations on the length of life of a single leaf, but each leaf probably lives for several years. By contrast, a Mango tree, which also produces new leaves about once a year, does so in great profusion, and the old leaves all fall soon afterwards. A Durian tree in Singapore will produce new leafy twigs at variable intervals of a few months, and its leaves are probably not long-lived; but nobody knows the normal length of life of a Durian leaf.

In the very uniform climate of Singapore, where grass grows throughout the year, one might expect trees also to grow continuously. In fact, some trees do this, but they are few. Most trees are like the Durian and the Mangosteen, and produce their new leaves in flushes at intervals. One of the exceptions is the Tĕmbusu, which goes on producing leaves slowly all the year round, though perhaps the process is more rapid in the wetter part of the year. Another exception is the Nutmeg tree.

What determines the intervals between successive new flushes of leaves? Clearly, the nature of the tree itself is the most important factor, seeing that under identical climatic conditions all trees do not behave alike. But evergreen trees of one kind commonly do behave alike, even in Singapore. If one Mangosteen tree has new leaves, the others (or most of them) will do the same. (Some trees may have a full flush of young leaves, others only on some of the branches; such minor differences of behaviour may be due to differences in the situation or earlier history of particular trees.)

But in trees which do not grow continuously, resumption of growth after a resting period must be due to some stimulus. The difference between trees is that they have different degrees of sensitivity to a stimulus; some will resume leafy growth on slight provocation, some need to be more strongly moved. It may be that the nature of the stimulus is not the same for all trees, but it seems probable that for most trees in Malaya the stimulus is rain following a dry period. Present knowledge of the behaviour of trees is insufficient for a more definite statement. Then again trees differ in the rapidity with which they respond to this kind of stimulus. Trees of *Saraca taipingensis* certainly respond in about two weeks, and (in Singapore) produce new leaf growth several times in a year, at irregular intervals, the amount of new growth at any time varying according to the circumstances (duration of rainy weather, time since last new growth, and perhaps other factors).

In Singapore, the most constant feature of the climate is a wet period from October to January. In this period there is rain nearly every day, and the ground is constantly moist, at least in sheltered places. At this season, practically all the smaller trees in the primitive forest produce new leaves. These plants live under the shade of the larger trees, and the continuous wet weather of October to January probably affects them more than those in the open, which are subject to the drying effect of bright sunlight part of the time.

A feature of young foliage in Malaya is its colour. In many cases it is light green, but in a considerable proportion it is pink or red. Bright colouring of young leaves is far more common here than in temperate regions. Among common trees of open country, the wild Cinnamon is one of the most striking examples. These trees are very abundant in Singapore, but apparently less so in some other parts of Malaya. The very young leaves are bright red, gradually fading until when full-grown they are very pale green; the full green colour then gradually develops. Another tree which has strikingly beautiful young foliage is the Ceylon Iron-wood or Pěnaga (*Mesua ferrea*). Many other trees have purplish or reddish young leaves.

Young leaves commonly have another distinctive character. They hang limply down from the supporting twigs until they reach their full size, and then gradually become stiff and move into an oblique position. It is naturally convenient for the leaf to complete growth in size before the rigid supporting skeleton of fibrous tissue is developed. But in certain trees it is not merely each new leaf that hangs limply down in this way. The twig that supports a number of new leaves may also hang limply until its growth is complete. The result is a tassel of limp, sometimes coloured new leaves, all hanging close together until the whole group is full-grown, after which the twig stiffens and moves into an oblique position, the leaves spreading on each side of it. This occurs especially in trees of the Leguminosae family. The common Jiring trees behave in this way, their young leaves being crimson-purple. The young leaves of *Saraca taipingensis* are more striking, as they are a delicate mauve beneath and a pretty pale green on the upper surface.

Some years ago, in Ceylon, observations were made on the temperature on the limply hanging red young leaves of various trees. It had been thought that the hanging position protected the leaves from the heating effect of the overhead midday sun. But in fact it was proved that some of these young leaves were actually hotter inside than the ordinary foliage of the tree. This extra heat is probably due to the red colour. The result of the higher temperature combined with the lack of firm covering of the young leaves must result in a greater loss of water by these leaves than from the tough older leaves. This water comes from the roots, and ascends the trunk and branches of the tree. The water has dissolved in it a small quantity of mineral salts, and these are needed by the young leaves. It is suggested that the extra evaporation experienced by these leaves is actually an advantage to them. But in fact we really do not know very much about the matter.

In Ceylon it has been reported that Cinnamon trees produce their new leaves always in dry periods, and this is true also of some other trees with red young leaves. But in the case of Saraca, which has coloured young leaves, I am sure that rainy weather is the stimulus. Observations in Malaya on wild Cinnamon trees, and others with bright red young leaves, are needed, to discover what relation the production of new leaves has to climatic change. Such relation may not be easy to establish.

We conclude then that evergreen trees grow new leafy twigs at intervals which depend partly on the nature of the tree and partly on external circumstances which provide stimuli. But trees have flowers and fruit as well as leaves, and most trees do not flower continuously. What makes them flower? The answer is partly the same. Frequency of flowering depends both on the nature of the tree and on external circumstances. But the stimulus to flowering is not always the same as the stimulus to new leaf growth, though it may be so in some cases. And in the case of flowering there are really two things that have to be considered: first, the formation of a flower-bud with the beginnings of a flower (or flowers) inside it; and second, the development of the bud to flowering. Sometimes one kind of stimulus causes bud development; the buds then rest and a quite different stimulus causes them to open. This certainly occurs in the case of some Malayan orchids (Chapter 10). The full details of such processes have been worked out for the flowering bulbs which are so much grown in Holland (daffodils, etc.), and in some measure for the fruit trees grown in temperate regions, but little is known about them in the case of Malayan trees. The only thing one can say with certainty is that in most cases the stimulus to flowering in evergreen trees is dry weather, and especially dry weather following suddenly upon a wet period.

Most probably the stimulus is perceived by the leaves (which lose water by evaporation and are immediately affected by dry weather), and transmitted from leaves to flower-buds, which may have been formed in the leaf-axils. The stimulus from leaf to flower-bud may be in the form of a hormone made in the leaves owing to dry conditions; but this is only a guess.

The case of the Tĕmbusu trees which are abundant in Singapore is a striking one. These trees flower gregariously and abundantly every year about May. There is no other tree-flowering which is so abundant or so regular in this island. The stimulus to flowering appears to be a week's dry weather following suddenly the end of the wet season, usually in January. It takes four months for this stimulus to have effect in flowering. I have noted that the time of flowering in different years varies slightly, and the variation depends on the date of the first dry week in January. Sometimes there is not a clear dry week, but more than one shorter dry period, and then flowering is irregular. In 1950 there was little dry weather in January but a dry period in February; the result has been a little scattered flowering in May and a heavy flowering in June.

An example of rapid response to the same stimulus is *Sterculia rubiginosa*, a small tree occasionally found in secondary thickets. This tree flowers within two or three weeks after the first short spell of dry weather in January, and is later conspicuous because of its brilliant scarlet fruits which open and exhibit (for a short time) dangling glistening seeds. (This is one of the trees called Tangisong Burong because though attractive their beads afford no food, but birds do eat Sterculia seeds.)

It is well known that in Penang the fruit season comes in the middle of the year. Fruits are formed from flowers, and the flowers of the fruit-trees are produced owing to the stimulus of dry weather early in the year. In Singapore, however, the fruit seasons are much less regular. Good fruit crops usually occur either about the middle of the year or about December–January. These fruit seasons correspond to the occurrence of dry weather, which is most frequent about February or in July–August. But sometimes there is not enough dry weather at either season to induce trees to flower, and then we may have eighteen months or even two years between two good crops of Durians and

Mangosteens. In 1946, on the other hand, when July had only half an inch of rain, there were two good crops of Durians, but this is rare. Rambutans (at least some kinds) seem to respond to a lesser spell of dry weather, and two crops a year, or even a larger number of small crops, are not uncommon. There are, of course, some evergreen trees that flower and fruit a little all the time. Such are the Chiku, Guava, and Pomelo. But it may be that in these also flowering is in some way controlled by an external stimulus.

Then we have the strange case of the wild fig trees that bear fruit on the trunk. There are two common kinds, *Ficus variegata* and *Ficus fistulosa*. *F. fistulosa* is a small tree with hollow twigs which are easily snapped; it fruits on short branches on the trunk throughout the year. *F. variegata* is a much larger tree, and only begins to fruit when it has surpassed the full height of the other species. Some trees of *F. variegata* have as many as six crops of fruit on the trunk in a year, as if one crop followed as soon as the preceding had fallen. These are gall-figs (see Chapter 7, and Corner's *Wayside Trees of Malaya*, p. 660). The seed-bearing figs of the same species (borne on separate trees) come only in one or two crops in the year, and perhaps may be dependent on a climatic stimulus.

It seems in general that flowering of evergreen trees is independent of new growth. In such cases, buds which will produce flowers only (not leaves) are formed on the branches behind the leaves, or in the axils of leaves already fully developed, not during the development of a flush of new leaves. But there are cases in which flowering occurs on the new leafy twigs along with the development of new leaves; and then the flowering and leafing are a response to the same stimulus. This is apparently the case with the Bachang, a Malayan relative of the Mango, which produces beautiful pink flowers with delicate green young leaves (sometimes leaves without flowers) at irregular intervals. But it will usually be found that Bachang trees in the same area flower together. I do not understand the behaviour of these trees.

The tallest trees of the primary forest usually have small flowers, and their flowering does not make a bright show of colour. I sometimes find people will not believe that all forest trees have flowers, and this is not very surprising. In fact, some individual trees flower at quite long intervals, especially in Singapore where climate stimuli are slight. I have known Shorea trees (which give the various grades of Měranti timber) which flowered only once in four or five years; and one tree of the genus Homalium flowered once in a period of twelve years.

Turning from native Malayan trees to garden shrubs (most of which are not native) we find the same kind of flowering pattern. A few kinds of shrubs, such as Allamanda and the common magenta Bougainvillaea, flower quite continuously, but most shrubs flower in response to dry weather. Some are quite sensitive, an example being the crimson Bougainvillaea (Mrs. Butt). In such cases, cultivation in a pot, which limits the growth of roots, and restriction of watering, is sufficient to induce flowering. Dry weather, or artificial drought in the case of pot plants, has its first effect on leaves, and the leaves must in some way transmit a stimulus to the buds which are to produce flowers. A change of soil conditions is enough to produce flowering in some cases. Oleander plants in sandy soil flower throughout the year; in a well-cultivated clay soil containing plenty of organic matter they grow vigorously without flowering. The sandy soil quickly dries after rain and provides the effect of nearly continuous drought.

Why should shrubs and trees flower in response to dry weather? The only answer I can think of is that dry weather affords the best chance that effective pollination will take place, so that a tree flowering in dry weather will have the best chance of producing a crop of fruits and seeds. Such a habit might well arise in a climate like that of Penang, with three fairly dry months every year (January–March). But in the south of Malaya the dry weather may have passed before the stimulus to flowering has had its effect. One would hardly expect the habit to develop under such conditions. In the case of Bougainvillaea, I have noted that seeds are produced in Singapore only during dry weather. These are plants native of countries with a fairly long dry season. In the case of Indian Mangoes also, it seems that dry weather at the time of flowering is necessary if fruit is to be formed. This partly explains why such Mangoes rarely fruit in Singapore. If there is enough dry weather to make them flower, it will probably be wet again by the time the flowers are open. Our Malayan Mangoes and their allies are evidently less sensitive to rain at the time of flowering. This seems to me a good reason why an attempt should be made to hybridize Malayan and Indian Mangoes. We might ultimately get a kind of good Mango that would fruit freely in our wet climate.

Turning now from flowers to seeds, the evergreen forest has another peculiarity. Probably in the majority of cases, seeds of our big forest trees do not rest. They germinate as soon as they fall to the ground. In many cases, they are actually incapable of resting, and if one attempts to rest them artificially by keeping them dry, they die. You can kill a durian seed by putting it in the full sun for a day or two, but if you plant it as soon as it is out of the fruit, it will germinate immediately. Seeds normally serve two purposes: they can be dispersed so that they can grow in places away from the parent plant, and they can remain dormant (resting) during a dry or cold period, growing when suitable weather returns. In Malaya the second purpose is unnecessary, as germination in the forest is possible at all times of the year. This is part of the evergreen way of life.

The evergreen way of life would seem to mean that a plant can go on growing indefinitely. What is there to limit its life? And in fact short-lived plants, such as the annuals and biennials of temperate regions, are quite lacking in the Malayan forest. Some short-lived plants grow in open places when forest has been cleared, or as weeds in cultivated land; they are followers of man, and most have been introduced (often accidentally) by man. In our gardens we grow short-lived plants which in temperate regions are called herbaceous annuals. But we can plant them at any time of year, and in about three months they produce their seeds and die; so we can have three or more generations in a year and the word annual is no longer appropriate. It is actually possible to make some annuals immortal, by making cuttings of their branches. This can be done with African Marigolds, and even with cabbages. These plants seem to be in some measure limited by their roots; if a stem-cutting can get new roots and if its buds are not all used up by flowering, it can go on growing.

But of course even the biggest forest trees do not live for ever. Sooner or later, their roots or their trunks become attacked by fungus parasites, which usually enter through a wound (caused perhaps by the fall of another tree). Then termites may join the attack, and finally the giant falls, giving room for another to grow. In contrast to the big trees, a herb like a wild ginger can be truly immortal. It has a creeping stem which produces erect leafy shoots of limited life; the old part of the stem dies, but the growing end can go on for ever provided it has suitable soil conditions. This case is discussed in detail in Chapter 3.

Now let us turn to the trees which are not evergreen in Malaya; that is, trees which are sometimes, if even for a very short period, bare of leaves. In most parts of the world, there is a season—the dry or cold season—in which all such trees are bare. But this is not true in Malaya, and those trees which from time to time are bare are just as varied in their habits as the evergreen trees. There is, however, this exception, that in the extreme north of Malaya there is a regular season at which nearly all deciduous trees are bare, namely the dry season of January–February. Even in Penang there are some deciduous trees which are not bound by this season, and as one travels southwards the irregularity of deciduous trees increases, probably reaching its most extreme condition in Singapore.

In the north of Malaya, Dadap trees (*Erythrina indica*) lose their leaves in December–January, and when bare become covered with scarlet flowers, followed by their curious pods (swollen at each seed) which ripen before the new leaf-growth begins. Flame trees are nearly all in flower in January and February. In Kedah, the *Cassia grandis* trees (not native) bear rose-pink flowers on their bare branches in February, and all the Rubber trees are wintering. In Pahang, where the driest month is July, trees of *Cassia nodosa*, with their lovely pale pink flowers, are bare for a short time about June; the flowers and young leaves then grow together. In Penang, the great Angsana trees (*Pterocarpus indicus*), which form such fine avenues, are not quite simultaneous in losing their leaves, and are bare for a short time only. They have a wonderful series of flowerings; during each flowering every tree which is at the right stage of development is covered for one day with a sheet of gold. The flowers come with the very young leaves, and always in the early months of the year. But in Singapore our few Angsana trees (few because of a serious disease which killed so many in the decade 1918–28) are very irregular and rarely give us a spectacular display.

In Singapore, the great majority of deciduous trees are bare for a few days only; and most of them have no respect for the calendar in timing their leaf-fall. If you look at one of our avenues of Flame trees at any time of year, you will find some trees in flower; but you will never see all in flower together. Limited observations made to date indicate that each tree flowers about every nine or ten months. The trees are grown from seeds and they are not quite alike in habit of growth and in the time at which they begin to flower. The result is that even an avenue of trees all planted simultaneously do not behave alike. The same is true of our avenues of Bungor trees (*Lagerstroemia flos-reginae*). Here also each tree flowers about every nine months, but different trees do not behave exactly alike, and even if the trees of an avenue begin by flowering together, they soon get out of step with each other, so that flowering of one or more trees may be found at any time of the year. Dadap trees in Singapore are rarely (if ever) wholly bare and flowering is casual and slight.

As noted above, evergreen trees develop new leafy twigs in response (usually) to wet weather, and flowers in response to dry weather; the two responses are in most cases quite independent of each other. In deciduous trees, however, the flowers are always borne at a definite stage in the leaf-cycle, either while the trees are bare (Dadap), or with the very young leaves (Flame tree), or when new leaf-growth is complete (Bungor). Flowering is therefore dependent on leaf-fall or on leaf-renewal, and it is more regular for an individual tree (in Singapore) than is the flowering of an evergreen. The amount of flowers borne by a Flame tree depends probably on the weather in the period just before leaf-fall, at which time the flower-buds are being formed.

It is interesting that some deciduous trees are more independent of climate than others. One of the most dependent on such change is the Rubber tree, which responds to our capricious dry seasons by an equally capricious behaviour. Any dry spell will cause some Rubber trees in Singapore to lose their leaves, at least on some branches, but it rarely or never happens that all Rubber trees on the island are bare simultaneously, though this happens every year in the north of Malaya. The reason for this erratic behaviour is that the response of each tree depends on its particular nature and also on its past history, and on the particular conditions under which it is growing (soil, exposure, etc.). It is well known that budded Rubber trees are more uniform in their behaviour than mixed seedlings. I observed four Rubber trees for a period of twelve years in Singapore. One of them changed its leaves on an odd branch or two frequently, but was never wholly bare. Two others sometimes did this and sometimes had a complete change; they did not always agree in the time of complete change. The fourth tree had leaf-changes at fairly regular periods averaging rather more than thirteen months. This last is very unusual; most Rubber trees seem to have a minimum length of life for their leaves of about five months; after that, dry weather is liable to cause leaf-fall.

The majority of trees from more seasonal climates do not adapt themselves very well to our uniform climate in Malaya, in some cases perhaps because our minimum lowland temperature is too high, in others because there is no dry season in which they can rest. Some will grow well enough, but do not flower well. This is especially true of trees from subtropical regions grown at our hill stations, where the average temperature is about right for them; the lack of seasonal change prevents them flowering normally. This is true of some Australian Eucalypts and Acacias in the Cameron Highlands.

Two curious cases are worth mentioning. One is the Indian Silk-cotton tree (*Bombax malabaricum*). In India this species is bare for several months in the dry season, and flowers and fruits while wholly bare. In Singapore we have two trees, and I noted their behaviour for several years. They did not behave quite alike, though growing side by side. Each tree remained bare for four months or more after leaf-fall, and the length of time between one leaf-renewal and the next averaged about nine and a half months for one tree and ten and a half months for the other. Thus the bare period might happen at any time of year, and was quite independent of climatic conditions. These trees, therefore, have an obligate resting stage, which the climate of Singapore may shorten a little, but cannot eliminate. The case of Gladiolus, reported elsewhere, is similar. The other peculiar case is an English Oak tree. I have kept a young Oak tree in a pot for about two years (it is still alive at the time of writing). When it arrived from England, it was bare of leaves, but a number of new leafy twigs soon developed (they were attacked by various of our local insects). After about five months, the leaves faded and fell, but before this occurred another set of leafy branches began to grow, from buds which had until then remained dormant. This procedure continued. There has never been a time when the tree was bare; it usually has had branches of two or three different ages, and the leaves on each have lasted about five months; and there have always been some resting buds. Thus the Oak tree has made a good effort to adopt the evergreen way of life, but I fear it would not live long in the open ground, exposed to full sun and rain and to the attacks of the local fauna.

Summarizing the above remarks, one may say that our climate, uniform on the average but with much small variation from place to place, and from year to year in one place, offers opportunity for varied response by the very large number of kinds of trees, both native and introduced, evergreen and deciduous, which we have in Malaya. The picture is an entirely different one from that in a temperate or subtropical climate with a constant cycle of strongly marked seasonal change. The number of recorded observations on the behaviour of our many trees in different places is very small. Anyone who is interested can obtain further new information if he will take the trouble to record regularly the behaviour of particular trees for a few years, and also make sure that meteorological data are also available for the same locality. It will soon be apparent which trees respond by their behaviour to climatic stimuli; but a decision as to the exact relationship between stimulus and response may not be at all easy to establish.

We should not conclude this chapter about the evergreen plant life of Malaya without some reference to the basic significance to all life of that universal greenness. This subject is dealt with in all elementary books on biology, but for the benefit of any reader who is not familiar with it a brief statement of the facts is given in the following paragraphs.

By virtue of the green pigment which they contain, leaves have the power of absorbing energy from sunlight and of using that energy to manufacture sugar from carbon dioxide and water. This is a process which no man-made factory can achieve, and on this process all other living organisms (man, animals, and plants which are not green) are entirely dependent for their life.

Leaves of plants take carbon dioxide from the air. In their surface they have special openings (called stomata) which allow air to enter, and there is a system of internal air-spaces in a leaf, so that every living cell of the leaf is in contact with the air. The cells absorb the carbon dioxide as fast as it enters the intercellular spaces. At the same time leaves are receiving water absorbed by the roots, and some of this water evaporates into the intercellular spaces, the vapour diffusing out through the stomata into the atmosphere. Dissolved in the water from the roots are simple salts, in very dilute solution. When the water evaporates, these salts remain.

The green cells of the leaf thus have at their disposal carbon dioxide from the air, water and salts from the roots. Using the energy from sunlight, the green cells are able to combine carbon dioxide and water to form sugar, which is then transformed to starch for storage if necessary. The cells of the leaf are able to combine the sugar with materials from the salts to form other more complex substances needed for food by the plant. The leaves are thus the chemical factories of the plant, but the whole of their activity depends ultimately on their power of absorbing energy from light and using it to make sugar. The sugar then acts as a store of energy (all food is stored energy) which can be used at any time by the plant for other purposes.

The food made by the leaves is transported to the other parts of the plant. There may be more food made during the hours of daylight than can be immediately transported; this is temporarily stored during the day and transported during the night. It goes to the parts of the plant where growth is taking place. Thus there is a two-way movement in leaves; water with dissolved salts is coming in, and food is going out, down the leaf-stalk to other parts of the plant. Some of the food is ultimately stored in seeds or tubers. Animals eat the food built up by plants, whether in leaves, seeds, or tubers. Man also eats plants, or eats animals which live on plants. So that the life of man is dependent on the work done by the green leaf. Agriculture is the basic industry of mankind, and must continue to be so, at least until men are clever enough to do in a factory what the green leaf now does for them.

Efficiency in agriculture depends on growing plants which give the greatest return of good food in proportion to the area of ground they occupy; the ease with which the food can be harvested is another consideration. The great wealth of green in Malaya means a great absorption and storage of energy, continued without interruption throughout the year. But a great proportion of that stored energy is of no obvious use to man. If man is ingenious enough, he may find uses for it. But man has found how to produce new kinds of plants which are more efficient for his purposes than those provided by nature. This process has developed greatly in temperate regions, but little in the wet tropics. When man has produced new and (from his standpoint) more efficient plants which are suited to grow in Malaya, man will be able to take full advantage of the evergreen character of the country. This matter is further discussed in Chapter 6.

CHAPTER TWO

ROOTS AND STEMS:
TREES, PALMS, PANDANS, AND TREE-FERNS

I F we compare an ordinary tree and a palm, we note at once
the striking difference that a palm has an unbranched trunk
with a single group of leaves at the top, whereas a tree bears
many branches with many much smaller leaves at the ends of
the branches. But there is another difference. The trunk of a
tree becomes gradually thicker as long as the tree lives. The
trunk of a palm does not increase in thickness once it is formed,
no matter how long the palm lives. This difference in behaviour
goes along with a difference in internal structure, which is really
the determining factor. And there is also another consideration
which is often overlooked. Just as the trunk of a palm does not
increase in thickness, so also its roots do not grow thicker as
they grow older. This also has an important bearing on the life
of the palm.

In Malaya, there are many plants which lack this power of
increase in thickness. Apart from palms, there are pandans,
bamboos, grasses, gingers, orchids, and the members of the
Arum or Kĕladi family. All these are common and conspicuous
plants in this country. Some of them are dealt with in the next
chapter. Here we will begin by a comparison of trees and palms,
based on the structure of both stem and roots.

We begin with the seed of a tree. A Rubber tree will do as
an example; some other trees would differ in details of seed-
structure and development, but these are unimportant for our
present purpose. The Rubber seed contains an embryo, or
young plant, and also a store of food to start that young plant in
life. The store of food is dry, and as such is not immediately
available to the embryo. Now if we soak the seed in water, the
food store in the seed takes up some of the water, and as a result
some of the food changes into a soluble condition and can be

absorbed by the embryo, which begins to grow. The embryo consists of two thin leaves, a very small root, and a bud which will form the erect leafy shoot. The root first pushes its way out of the seed, and immediately turns downwards. The two thin leaves of the embryo (they are called cotyledons) remain in the seed, in contact with the food store, and their job is to absorb this food and pass it on to the growing root and shoot. The cotyledons elongate just enough to allow the shoot-bud to become free from the seed, and the shoot then grows upwards. As soon as it reaches the light, above the surface of the ground, it turns green, and it soon bears the first green leaves of the tree (Fig. 1, a, a^1). We then have a seedling with root growing downwards and leafy stem growing upwards. By the time the seedling has green leaves of its own, it becomes independent of the food store in the seed.

The downward-growing root is continuous in a vertical line with the upward-growing stem. Soon the root produces branches, growing from its sides, and somewhat later the stem also produces branches. As the seedling grows in height, so the stem (and the main root which is continuous with it) grows in thickness. If we cut through the stem when it is half an inch or so in thickness, we see that the middle part is composed of wood, except for a small central pith. As everyone knows, the main part of the trunk of a tree consists of wood, and the part outside the wood is commonly called bark. The matter is not quite so simple as that, as we shall see shortly, but let us confine our attention to the wood for the present. As the wood increases in thickness, new wood must be continually added *on the outside*. This is a form of growth, and growth consists in an increase of the number of cells in the wood. A new cell can only be formed by the enlargement and then the division of an existing cell, the result being two cells instead of one; and the process can be repeated. Growth implies division of cells; and the dividing cell must be perennially youthful and active. The woody cells which are formed by its activity develop tough thick walls, and then they lose the power of growth and division.

Growth then is continually taking place, by division of cells, on the outside of the woody cylinder of the stem. As this cylinder gets larger, the zone of active dividing cells gets pushed

Fig. 1—(a) rubber seedling × ½; (a¹) cotyledons removed from germinating rubber seed × ½; (b) germinating coconut × ¼; (b¹) same in section.

C

outwards, and its circle becomes larger. This process goes on, both in stem (or trunk) and roots, throughout the life of the tree. The active dividing cells are called *cambium*. The wood is called *xylem* by botanists (xylon is the Greek word for wood). Everyone knows that the wood of the tree is needed to support the branches; but the wood also has another very important work to do: it carries water from the roots to the leaves, which are continually losing water by evaporation to the air. The water travels along many tubes which are embedded in the firm substance of the wood.

What happens outside the cambium, which itself is continuously being pushed outwards by the wood it produces? The cambium does a double duty. It not only produces wood, but also it produces, *on the outside*, cells of another kind called *phloem*. The phloem cells carry food made in the leaves to the parts of the plant which need it: to the cambium itself, and to the growing-points at the tips of stems and roots. In the case of the Rubber tree, the latex is produced in a special network of cells in the phloem, distinct from the normal food-conducting cells. We still do not know what use the latex is to the tree; why a Rubber tree should need to produce latex when other trees do not and are apparently no worse for the lack of it.

The phloem is still not quite the end of the story. Outside the phloem is another cambium, which produces new cells on the outside only; these cells develop walls made of cork and then die, and they form the true bark of the tree (Fig. 2c). The bark is a protective layer; it protects the phloem beneath it, and also the actively growing true cambium. As the trunk of the tree increases in girth, the bark (which is dead) is stretched, and it usually cracks, but the cracks are repaired by the new bark growing underneath. So between the wood and the true bark of the tree, in a comparatively thin layer, is active tissue constantly renewed by the activity of the cambium, and this is true throughout the life of the tree. And this active tissue is continuous downwards from the trunk to the root and to its branches.

It is because of the presence of cambium that bud-grafting of Rubber trees and other trees (such as Rambutans) is possible. The essential feature of bud-grafting is the union of the cambium of the bud with the cambium of the stock. Because both are actively growing tissues, they have the power of uniting. This question is further discussed in Chapter 5.

Now let us consider the series of events of seedling development and the growth of root and stem in a palm tree; we will take the Coconut palm as an example. There is an embryo in a Coconut, just as in a Rubber seed, and with the embryo is a lot of food (the meat of the Coconut). But the embryo has only one cotyledon, for which reason palms and other plants which are related to them are called *monocotyledons*, and plants which have two cotyledons in the embryo are called *dicotyledons*. The differences between monocotyledons and dicotyledons are many; the difference in the embryo is only one of them, but it is selected for the purpose of naming the two classes of plants. The difference of development and plant-structure between a palm and a Rubber tree expresses another of the great differences between the two classes. It is a pity that we have to use these two ugly and cumbersome words dicotyledons and monocotyledons to distinguish the two great divisions of flowering plants; but these names are in universal use and there are no other accepted ones which can be substituted for them.

The cotyledon of the Coconut remains almost entirely inside the nut, just as the two cotyledons remain in the Rubber seed, and like them it absorbs food from the store provided in the Coconut. While absorbing food, the cotyledon increases greatly in size (Fig. 1, *b*, *b*¹). The root of the embryo grows out from the seed and then downwards, and the leaf-shoot begins to grow upwards. But now come two differences from the Rubber seedling. The shoot of the Coconut does not grow upwards rapidly, bearing a number of small leaves; it remains very short, and produces a succession of rather large leaves that grow upright. Though it grows upwards very slowly, the top of the shoot (or stem) itself increases in width; its shape is that of an inverted cone (Fig. 2a). The primary root of the embryo is naturally quite small. It has no cambium, and so cannot increase in thickness. It is soon too small to be able to supply all the water needed by the young plant. Another root is therefore needed, and that root would be useless as a branch on the first root; the second root must therefore grow from the base of the shoot or stem of the young plant. This second root also soon becomes inadequate, owing to the growth of large leaves, and then a third and a fourth root grow from the base of the stem. After that, a palm stem continues to produce new roots near its base for the rest of its life. All these roots may have small branches, but the branches of any one root cannot supply a greater amount of water than will pass through the base of the root which is joined to the stem; and this base, owing to the lack of cambium, has a limited thickness.

Now let us turn to the development of the stem. It continues the inverted-cone shape for two or three years, its top becoming larger and larger, producing larger and larger leaves until leaves equal in size to those of a full-grown palm are produced. Now the stem has attained its full diameter, and it begins to grow upwards to form the trunk of the palm. An old Coconut trunk has a series of rings on it. These rings are the scars which show where successive leaves were attached. The base of each leaf is a sheath, and the attachment of the sheath encircles the trunk. The distance between one ring and the next is the amount the trunk grew in height between forming one leaf and the next.

The next question is, how does the structure of the palm trunk compare with that of the Rubber tree? Both trunks have xylem which contains water-conducting channels, and also phloem which conducts food, but these tissues are differently arranged. In the Rubber tree the xylem forms an ever-enlarging woody cylinder, with all the phloem outside it. In the palm trunk, strands consisting of both xylem and phloem, a few cells of each, are scattered throughout, but more densely towards the outer part of the trunk. With each strand is also a strand of fibres, and the fibres are especially developed towards the outside of the trunk, where they actually become so numerous that the strands of conducting cells are embedded in a solid mass of tough fibres. The fibres form the strong part of the palm trunk, just as the woody cylinder is the strong part of a Rubber tree. As the palm has no cambium, it can place most of its strength right at the outside; but a Rubber tree cannot do this, as the outside has to be occupied by bark and phloem. The palm trunk has no bark; it does not need bark, as the fibrous outer layer is a suitable protection. If you compare a solid iron bar with a hollow cylinder or pipe made from the same amount of

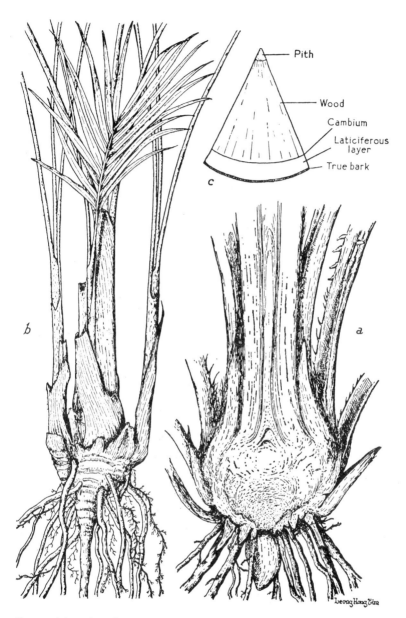

Pith

Wood

Cambium

Laticiferous
layer

True bark

c

b

a

FIG. 2—(a) section of young oil palm plant, with seed attached, showing short
stem with widening apex × ¾; (b) base of young branching palm, showing three
lateral branches × ½; (c) cross section of branch of rubber tree × 1.

iron, the latter is much more rigid. The Coconut palm, therefore, makes the best possible use of its strengthening material.
The Royal palm has a trunk which becomes wider above the
base. This widening is due to an increase in size of certain
cells in the trunk, not to any activity of a cambium, and once it
is formed it does not alter further.

Summarizing, the stem of the Rubber tree grows rapidly in
height from the very beginning, and increases in thickness afterwards, but the palm stem grows very slowly in height at first,
widening its top all the time, and only grows into a visible trunk
after attaining its full width; the main root of a Rubber seedling
also increases continuously in thickness and other roots are all
branches of the main root, but in the palm seedling the first root
is soon inadequate, and so other roots are produced on the base
of the stem.

A practical consequence of this peculiarity of the palm is very
important. If a palm seedling is well-nourished with manure in
the early stages, while the width of the stem is developing, the
base of the trunk, when it is formed, will be broad, and on this
broad base the future trunk can grow strongly. But if the seedling is starved during this early stage, the base of the trunk will
be small, and that deficiency can never be made good as the palm
tree grows older. Further, if at a later stage the roots of the
palm are starved or injured, the size of the growing top of the
trunk will be reduced, and the thinner part of the trunk can
never afterwards be altered; it will form a constriction, reducing
the efficiency of the whole plant, even if the roots subsequently
regain their vigour.

Turning now to the question of propagation, it is clear that
the peculiar structure of a palm makes the process of bud-
grafting impossible. First, the palm has only one bud, at the top
of the trunk, and to remove that would kill the palm. Second,
even if we could get a bud, there is nothing in a palm trunk on
which to graft it; there is no cambium or other actively growing
tissue with which a bud could unite.

A Coconut palm has normally a single trunk; freak palms
with a forked trunk are occasionally found, but they are rare.
But some other kinds of palm have many trunks; for example,
the Sago palm and the Nibong. In such cases, the extra trunks

are produced by buds from the very base of the first trunk; that is, from the inverted cone in which the trunk is building its broad base (Fig. 2b). Each bud which is to form a new trunk has itself to go through the same preliminary process of broadening its top before it can begin to form the trunk. One original Sago or Nibong plant can form ultimately a clump or even (in the case of Sago) a grove of trunks. Such a clump can be propagated by cutting off a portion of the base that has a young growth upon it, just as one can propagate a bamboo. In fact, these palms have almost adopted a bamboo habit. They differ from bamboos in having only one growing bud at the top of each trunk; and Nibong differs also in the fact that each trunk is able to continue growing in height indefinitely. We will consider the peculiarities of the bamboo way of growth in the next chapter.

One of the most peculiar of all palms is Nipah, which grows on muddy river banks near the sea, where the water at high tide is saline, but fresh at low tide. Nipah palms have no trunks; or rather, their trunks are horizontal, in the mud, and branched. Besides the leaves, the trunks bear erect flowering and fruiting branches; ultimately each of the latter bears a large spherical head of fruits, looking not unlike a fruiting head of the seashore Pandan.

Pandans have much in common with palms. Like palms, they form trunks and roots which cannot increase in thickness. Unlike palms, the trunks often branch above ground level, and new roots are also often produced above ground level. These above-ground roots grow obliquely downwards, and so form struts around the base of the Pandan trunk (Fig. 3b); they are much thicker than most palm roots. The need for these strut-roots in Pandans is due partly to the fact that the trunks are much more slender than palm trunks, and partly to the branching, which makes a top-heavy plant. Pandans are unlike palms also in their leaves, which are long and narrow, without leaflets. On the whole, Pandans are smaller than palms, but the big swamp Pandan called Mengkuang, with trunks sixty feet or more high and leaves twenty feet long, rivals most palms in bulk.

Though it is true that monocotyledons in general have no power of increase in thickness, a few of them do have a cambium; but it does not behave like the cambium of a Rubber tree. The

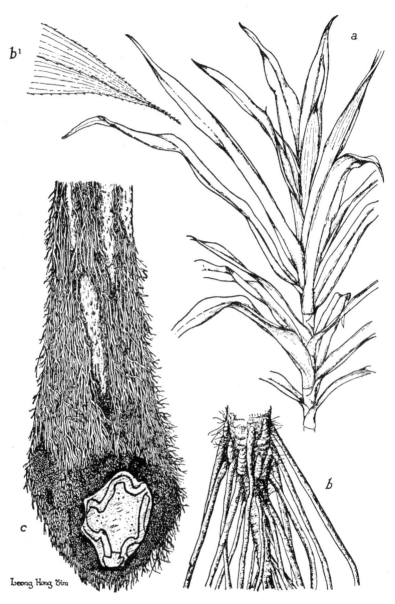

FIG. 3—(*a*) leafy tip of a *Dracaena* stem × ½; (*b*) base of stem of small pandan × ½; (*b*¹) tip of a pandan leaf × ½; (*c*) base of tree-fern trunk, cut through obliquely × ⅓.

stem first has scattered strands of conducting cells, each strand containing both xylem and phloem. When this structure is complete, a cambium becomes active near the surface of the stem. But instead of forming a solid cylinder of wood inside, and a layer of phloem outside, the cambium forms more strands like those already developed, each strand consisting of both xylem and phloem, with a reinforcement of fibres. These composite strands, packed closely together, are all developed on the inside of the cambium layer, which thus becomes pushed outwards; outside the cambium a layer of protective bark is formed.

A plant of this kind can grow into a tree with the usual type of trunk and branches, but the leaves are of the monocotyledon type, with close parallel veins. There are a few kinds of such trees in the forests of Malaya; they are called Dracaena (Fig. 3a). There are species of Dracaena also in other parts of the world; the most famous one is the Dragon tree of Teneriffe. A kind of shrubby plant, often called Dracaena, with variegated (often red) leaves, is common in Malayan gardens, and is often planted on Malay graves. This plant is properly called Cordyline; it differs from Dracaena in the structure of its fruits.

Some other monocotyledons which have the same kind of secondary increase in thickness never grow into trees of the usual branching type. One is the Sisal Hemp (Agave, from Mexico), which has a short thick stem bearing long stiff leaves with strong spiny tips. After a few years the top of the stem of an Agave ceases to form leaves, and produces instead a rapidly elongating flower-stalk fifteen feet or more tall, with many branches. This inflorescence produces its flowers and then its fruits, after the ripening of which the whole plant dies. Sisal hemp and a few other kinds of Agave are often grown in Malayan gardens. Their "hemp" consists of fibrous strands in the leaves.

Another quite different class of plants which have something of the palm habit are the Tree-ferns, which are so abundant and so beautiful in clearings at our hill stations. A tree-fern is like a palm in having a single trunk with a crown of large leaves at the top of it. But the leaves are very different from palm leaves. Palm leaves have a single row of leaflets on each side of the axis of the leaf; each leaflet is folded or pleated longitudinally. The base of each palm leaf forms a sheath which surrounds the trunk.

Tree-fern leaves have many more and much smaller leaflets than palms, and the leaflets are not pleated, nor does the base of the tree-fern leaf form a sheath. But of course the main difference is that the leaves of tree-ferns (or some of them) bear spores on their lower surface. Ferns have no flowers and so they have no fruits or seeds. They are reproduced by microscopic spores which are dispersed by the wind. The spores are produced in little sacs or sporangia which are seen in little brownish groups, arranged according to a regular pattern on the veins. We shall have more to say about these in Chapter 11.

Like palms, tree-fern trunks have no cambium and cannot grow in thickness in the way a tree does. But they do grow in thickness in a peculiar way of their own. As with palms, the tree-fern must grow roots from the trunk, because the original roots cannot increase in thickness and so are soon inadequate. But the tree-fern does not confine its roots to the base of the trunk. They grow out from almost the whole surface of the trunk, except the youngest parts just below the crown. They do not grow straight outwards, nor straight downwards, but become entangled with each other to form a very tough fibrous black cover for the trunk. Towards the base, this covering of interwoven roots is much thicker than the original trunk, and serves the same purpose as a secondary growth in thickness, combined with a greatly increased capacity for absorbing water. This tangled mass of roots also affords an excellent growing place for smaller ferns and orchids.

CHAPTER THREE

BAMBOO, GINGER, AND ORCHID

IN the last chapter we discussed the habit of a Rubber tree and a Coconut palm, and the way in which the habit is connected with the internal structure in each case. Next we will consider some other monocotyledons which agree with the palm in having no cambium in stem or root, but in which each erect leafy stem is of definite or limited growth; it grows so high and then stops. Further growth can then only come from the base of the plant. This is a very important growth-habit, and it is shown most conspicuously by bamboos, which we will deal with first.

If we compare a palm trunk with the stem (or culm) of a bamboo, we find the following differences. A Coconut palm trunk has rings on it, which are the scars of the bases of the leaves. The rings are fairly close together. The trunk is of about equal diameter from bottom (except the very base) to top, and it has no branches. Internally it is solid, but the outer tissues (consisting of closely packed fibres) are much firmer than the inner. A bamboo culm also has rings on it, but they are much further apart than those on the Coconut trunk. The culm tapers gradually from the bottom to the top, which is quite slender. At most of the upper rings (or nodes) there are branches. Internally the bamboo culm is hollow, the outer walls being extremely hard, but there is a firm cross-wall inside the culm at every node. The structure of the outer wall of the culm is very like the structure of the outer part of a palm trunk, having many small conducting strands embedded in a mass of hard fibres.

The small branches on a bamboo culm are leafy, and the leaves are very like grass leaves. In fact, bamboos and grasses belong to the same family of plants. A bamboo leaf has several distinct parts (Fig. 4a). The green blade, or leaf proper, is attached at its base to a sheath, which enfolds the stem and is joined to the stem along the whole circumference of a node. The blade is jointed to the sheath, and when old breaks off at the joint, leaving the sheath around the stem. Where blade and sheath meet, there is an upgrowth like a short continuation of the sheath across the base of the blade; this is called the *ligule*. Each edge of the blade, at the base, runs a little along the edge of the sheath, and sometimes then forms an outgrowth, like a little ear, called an *auricle*. The auricles sometimes bear long bristles.

Now if we look at a young culm that has grown to about half its full height, we see that it is covered with large sheaths, which protect the culm itself while it is soft and still elongating (Fig. $4a^1$). These sheaths are really modified leaves, and they all have blade, sheath, ligule, and auricles (Fig. $4a^2$). The ligule and auricles are large and easy to see, whereas on the foliage leaves they often are too small to see easily. Now different kinds of bamboos are at first glance very much alike, and it is not easy to pick out distinctive features. The most distinctive features are found to occur in the sheaths which protect the young culms, which is the reason these sheaths are here described in detail. Not only the shape and size of blade, ligule, and auricles, but also the colour of the sheath, and of the hairs which it bears, may give useful characters for recognizing a particular kind of bamboo. It should be noted in passing (though this is well known to anyone who has handled a bamboo) that the loose hairs on the backs of the culm-sheaths are very irritant if they come into contact with the softer parts of one's skin.

As the culm grows to its full height, the blades on the upper sheaths are successively longer, and sooner or later they are green; there is, in fact, a complete transition from culm-sheath to ordinary leaf. Under each sheath is a bud, which is enclosed by a much smaller protective sheath (another modified leaf). Sooner or later most of these buds will grow, but usually not until the culm has reached its full height, and has fully developed its fibrous walls. Then it has no more need of the protective sheaths, and these fall; after that the buds begin to grow and form branches, each branch again with nodes and leaves, each leaf with a sheath protecting the stem. Secondary branches then come, especially from the bases of the primary ones. The par-

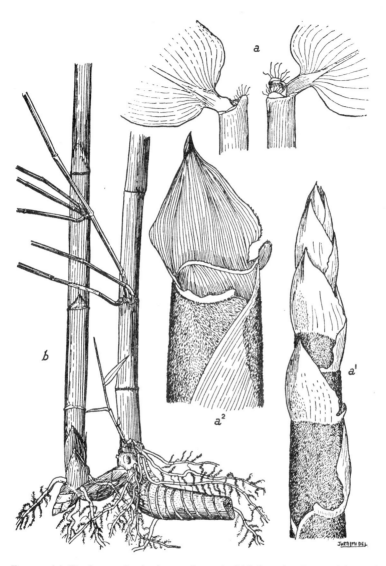

Fig. 4—(a) *Bambusa vulgaris:* bases of two leaf-blades, showing auricles and ligule $\times$ 1; (a^1) top of young growing culm $\times \frac{1}{4}$; (a^2) a single culm-sheath $\times \frac{1}{2}$; (b) part of a different bamboo, showing an old sheathless culm bearing branches, a young sheath-covered culm and a new bud at its base $\times \frac{1}{4}$.

ticular pattern of branching depends on the nature of the bamboo. Some common kinds of bamboos have no branches near the base of the main culms, but the thorny bamboo has long thorny branches in this position.

We have not yet mentioned the roots, nor the root-bearing base of the culm. This is most easily understood if we examine the origin and development of a new culm. At the base of an old bamboo clump, large buds may be found. These buds are covered with overlapping hairy sheaths; they are, in fact, the edible "bamboo shoots" which (when they are fully developed) are cut for the market. The buds develop slowly, and are packed inside with a solid mass of food material, which is to serve for the growth of the new culm. When all is ready, the bud probably waits for a period of wet weather, and then begins to grow into a culm. As there is a good supply of food already in the bud, growth can be rapid. In the bud, the bases of successive sheaths (the nodes) are very close together. As the bud grows, the internodes elongate, separating the base of one sheath from the base of the next. The top of the growing culm then appears as a pyramid of sheaths, the upper ones gradually emerging from the enfoldment of the lower.

A new culm at first grows slowly, but the rate of growth increases rapidly until it is a maximum when the culm is about half-grown. Measurements made at various places indicate that this maximum rate of growth is commonly about a foot in a day, and the giant bamboo at Peradeniya, Ceylon, was found to grow 46 cm. in a day. These speeds are only maintained for a few days, and then the rate of growth decreases gradually until the full height is reached.

While the culm is growing in height, roots are growing from its base. The base of the new culm has to grow for a short distance horizontally, to carry it clear of the older culms, after which the end bends upwards (Fig. 4b). In some kinds of bamboo, the new culms are very close to the old ones, so that the clump is very dense; in others the horizontal distance grown by the base of a new culm is greater, with the result that the culms are less crowded. In any case, in the very base of the culm the nodes are close together, and roots grow from these nodes. The roots are slender, and very numerous. They are essentially of the same nature as palm roots, and have to be numerous because they cannot increase in thickness. Many people call the whole base of a bamboo clump the "root". In fact, most of the base of the plant consists of the bases of the individual culms, one grown from another. In all the culm-bases the nodes are close together, and so the interior is solid; there is no room for a hollow between one node and the next, and the whole structure is very dense and hard. A new culm is formed by a bud which grows from one of the nodes at this tough basal part of the clump. It must grow from here because it must form new roots of its own, and these new roots must grow into the earth. Indefinite branching of the upper parts of culms would not be possible because there is a limit to the amount of water a culm can carry upwards, and a limit to the amount its own roots can supply; and upper branches cannot grow new roots of their own when they are far from the earth.

Bamboos are giant grasses, and they have grass-like flowers. But if you want to find bamboo flowers in Malaya, you may have to look for some time. A few kinds of local bamboo have a few flowers on some of the small branches of most culms, but others flower very rarely. The bamboo most grown for its edible shoots occasionally produces a culm with flowers on all its branches, and this is then conspicuous, but it is not a common sight. One Malayan bamboo, brought by Mr. Ridley some fifty years ago from Province Wellesley, and since grown in the Singapore Botanic Gardens, has never been seen to have flowers in all that time. In India, most bamboos flower at long intervals, of some-where about thirty years. When this occurs, all plants of one species in a district flower simultaneously, and after flowering they die. They produce quantities of seeds, which are rather like grains of wheat, and are edible. New plants grow from the seeds. So far as is known, Malayan bamboos never flower this way. But a number of plants of the thorny Indian bamboo in Penang did all flower together some years ago, and all died afterwards; it took them about three years to complete the process. Each new culm produced flowers and no leaves, and as a result the whole clump gradually grew weaker until it died. A different Indian bamboo planted in Singapore later behaved in the same way.

Now let us turn to the ginger family, of which there are about one hundred and fifty species in Malaya. They are very common plants in the forest, and some are village plants. All have the same general habit of growth, and in general pattern they resemble the habit of bamboos, with some differences. As an example, we will take the common village plant called Languas (the botanical name is *Languas galanga*).

A clump of Languas (Fig. 5*a*) is like a miniature bamboo clump. It consists of a number of erect leafy stems close together, but the leaves are larger than bamboo leaves, and the stems are not branched. As with a bamboo, each new erect stem starts as a bud from the base of an old one, and the growth of the new stem has to be a little in the horizontal direction before it grows upwards (Fig. 5*a*¹). Roots grow on this basal part of every stem. The whole of each stem is covered with the sheaths of its leaves (the sheaths overlap); it is never bare like an old bamboo culm. The base of each Languas stem is covered with sheaths which have no blade; the rest of the stem bears leaves which have blade, sheath, and ligule. Each stem of Languas is of limited growth. Some stems bear no flowers, but are leafy to the top. Other stems bear a head of many small flowers at the top of the stem.

In Languas, and more so in many other members of the ginger family, we see the horizontal basal part of each new stem as an essential part of the structure of the plant. A species in which this horizontal part of each new stem is better developed is *Catimbium muticum* (Fig. 6), one of the commonest wild gingers of rather wet ground (in thickets by ditches, etc.) of open places. In Catimbium, a bud arises at the base of a leafy stem, and this bud grows into a horizontal underground stem for a few inches; then the end turns upwards and forms an erect leafy stem like the one from which it sprang. The horizontal underground part of the stem is called a *rhizome*, because of its root-like appearance. But it is not a root; it is covered with sheaths which are comparable to the sheaths of a bamboo culm, and it bears roots. The rhizome is fleshy, not tough, and it contains a store of food, just as does the bud of the bamboo. The whole habit of the plant again is dependent on the internal structure. Because the roots do not increase in thickness, the

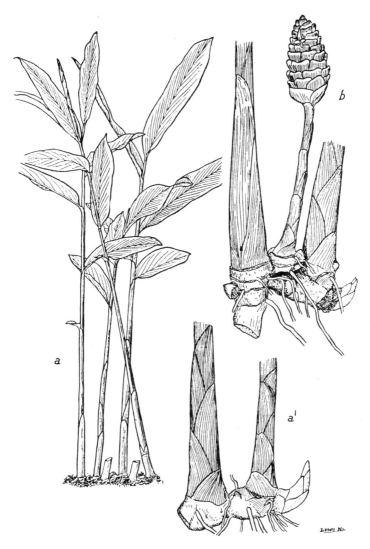

FIG. 5—(a) *Languas*: plant × ⅛; (a¹) part of base of plant × ½; (b) a village ginger: base of plant with inflorescence × ⅓.

D

stem must continually bear new roots; it is obviously of advantage, therefore, to have part of each stem horizontal in the ground to bear the roots it needs before it turns upwards and produces some leaves. And because each stem cannot increase in thickness, a limit must be set to the height of it and the number of leaves it bears. Such a plant as this is potentially immortal. The old parts die after a time, but the growing end can continue indefinitely.

It would obviously be a possible arrangement to have a continuously creeping rhizome, bearing erect side-shoots at intervals, the end never turning upwards. This does occur in some bamboos in China, and in many grasses, but it does not occur in the ginger family, nor among orchids. In the ginger family, each new part of the rhizome sooner or later turns up its end and forms a leafy stem, and the next piece of rhizome is formed from a bud from the base of the last leafy stem. Our garden Cannas, which belong to a related family, behave in the same way.

In the dry countries north of Malaya, and in East Java, members of this family lose their leaves in the dry season, as many trees do. This means that the whole of each erect leafy stem dies, and all that is left is the rhizome under the ground. The rhizome carries a store of food which will enable the plant to start its new growth of leafy stems at the next growing season. Most rhizomes in this family are aromatic, including the true ginger and Languas. These aromatic rhizomes are useful in human food and in medicine; but what good the aromatic substances are in the plants is not known.

Both Languas and Catimbium (Fig. 6b) have flowers at the top of their leafy stems. But many other members of the family have another way of flowering, especially those in the forest. In these plants, flowering stems are very short, and instead of leaves they have only short sheaths. The flowers are in a compact terminal head, which is either borne a short distance above the surface of the ground (Fig. 5b), or even partly embedded in the ground. In some cases, the flower head is more than half-buried; the base of each flower (which is tubular) is actually underground, but the top, with its brightly coloured floral parts, is just on the surface of the ground. In such a case, the fruits

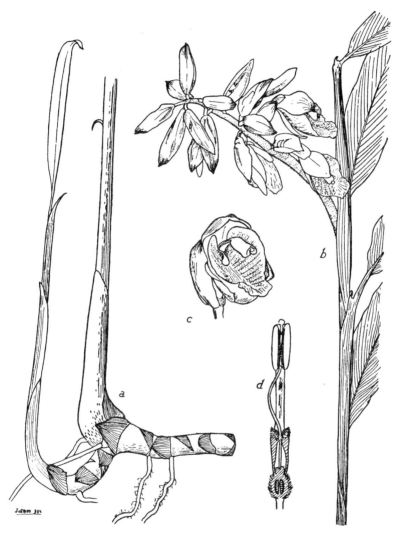

FIG. 6—*Catimbium muticum:* (*a*) base of plant, showing rhizome and a young leafy shoot × ½; (*b*) top of flowering stem × ½; (*c*) a single flower × 1; (*d*) section of base of flower, with petals removed, showing slender style in the flower-tube, and stamen joined to mouth of tube × 1½.

develop underground. Nobody knows how the seeds are dispersed.

The flowers of members of the ginger family are mostly fairly large, but they are all fragile, and last less than a day. The conspicuous part of each flower is formed from modified stamens; only one stamen is normally developed, and the stigma stands just above it (Fig. 6 *c*, *d*). The flowers are probably all insect-pollinated, but no observations of insect visits to the Malayan gingers have been published. The flowers of many gingers have a very orchid-like aspect, caused by the large lip and single stamen, but in fact the parts of the flower have different origins in gingers and orchids, and the two families are not very closely related, though doubtless derived from the same stock.

The orchid family is a very large one, the largest in the Malayan flora. Here we will consider only two of the common ground orchids, which have the same basic habit of growth as gingers, with differences in detail. We begin with Arundina, which is significantly called the bamboo orchid because of its likeness to a small clump of bamboo (Fig. 7).

An Arundina plant forms a clump of leafy stems, not unlike a dwarf bamboo, but the stems are very slender and solid and not branched, and there are normal leaves in place of the sheaths on the bamboo culm; also the top of the Arundina stem bears flowers, as in Languas. Each new leafy stem arises at the base of an old one, and has first a short thick root-bearing part, with very short internodes (Fig. 7*a*). The leaf-blades are jointed to their sheaths, and when old they fall, leaving the old stem covered with brown withered sheaths.

After an Arundina stem has finished flowering, it does not die, even though all the leaves have withered or fallen. Some of the buds (under the old sheaths) near the top of the stem then begin to grow into short leafy branches (Fig. 7*e*). They do so by breaking through the base of a sheath. Each such branch has a swollen base, and sooner or later this swollen base bears short roots. Now if the old stem is blown over or broken off, the branch will root directly into the ground, and a new plant will be formed; or the branch may eventually become detached, and fall to the ground. This is a method of vegetative propaga-

FIG. 7—*Arundina:* (a) bases of successive stems × ½; (b) top of flowering stem × ½; (c) flower × ½; (d) longitudinal section of flower × ½; (e) leafless old stem bearing a branch which can grow into a new plant × ½.

tion provided by the plant itself; and it is also the easiest way for a gardener to propagate these plants.

Now let us turn to the common ground orchid called Spathoglottis (Fig. 8). At first sight, this looks very different from Arundina. It has no erect slender stems, and all the leaves, which are rather large, appear to grow from the "root" of the plant, the tall erect flower-stalks appearing among the leaves. But if we look more closely at the growth of the plant, we find that it does have erect stems which bear the leaves, but the stems are very short and thick instead of long and slender; they are like the bases of Arundina stems. Each separate stem is bulb-shaped, and is sometimes called a *pseudobulb*, or false bulb. (A true bulb is like an onion, made of many separate fleshy leaves, but a pseudobulb is solid.) An old Spathoglottis pseudobulb has rings round it, rather close together in the basal part, more distant towards the top; it also bears roots towards the base (Fig. 8a). The rings are the leaf-scars; they correspond to the nodes on the stem of a bamboo. The leaves have each a basal sheath, which quite encloses the pseudobulb when it is young, and then a stalk, bearing the blade; there is a joint at the top of the sheath, and here the old leaf breaks off. If we look carefully at the pseudobulb, we find several buds, each on one of the rings. These buds can grow either into new pseudobulbs or into flower-stalks. Usually only one or two buds near the base grow into new pseudobulbs (Fig. 8b). If we took the Spathoglottis pseudobulbs and stretched them until they were long and slender, they would be very like the stems of Arundina, except that the top of the pseudobulb of Spathoglottis does not usually bear a flower-stalk (it does so occasionally). The flower-stalks normally all come from lateral buds (buds on the side of a pseudobulb).

The great majority of orchids, whether they grow in the earth or on trees, have this same habit of growth, which they share with bamboo and ginger. Different orchids differ in details of development of the parts of the plant, but the basic pattern is the same. Thus in some orchids, the length of rhizome between one leafy stem (or pseudobulb) and the next may be short, in others long; the pseudobulb itself may be short or long, round or flat, it may consist of one or many internodes;

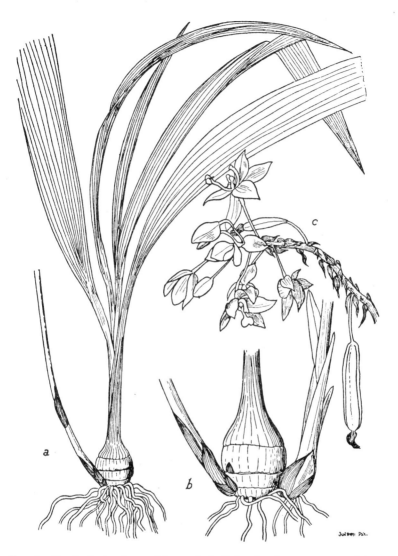

Fig. 8—*Spathoglottis plicata*: (a) pseudo-bulb bearing leaves, roots, and in-florescence-stalk × ⅓; (b) pseudo-bulb bearing new leafy shoot on right, in-florescence on left, and a resting bud × ⅔; (c) inflorescence × ½.

the flower-stalk (bearing one or many flowers) may be at the top of the pseudobulb, or upon its side, or from its base, or even from the rhizome between two pseudobulbs. There is one great exception to this general rule, and it is shown by our common Vanda Miss Joaquim (Fig. 9a), by the Malayan Scorpion orchids (genus Arachnis), and a number of related orchids. In these plants, which constitute the largest single tribe of orchids in Malaya, the tip of every stem goes on growing indefinitely, and all flowers are produced from lateral buds. Sometimes a lateral bud may grow into a branch of the stem, not into a flowering branch, but when it does so, the new branch of the stem can also go on growing indefinitely. Now let us consider some of the implications of this. As the stem becomes longer and longer (and never any thicker), it may not be efficiently supplied with water if all roots are at the base; and if the plant is to go on growing at the tip for many years, clearly it must grow roots above the base. In fact we find that all such orchids continue to bear roots at intervals throughout the length of the stem. After a number of years, the older parts of the stem may even die, but the tip can go on growing indefinitely, if it has the necessary supply of water and salts from its roots. If such a stem has fairly long internodes, it must increase fairly rapidly in length. It then soon grows too long to support itself, and either it must creep on the ground or support itself on a tree. The roots borne by the stems of these orchids are adapted to live in the air, so that they can be produced high above the ground; and also they are adapted to attach themselves to the bark of a tree; they are, in fact, climbing roots, and these orchids, if they develop long stems, are climbers. An Arachnis plant can climb to the top of a tree, and there raise its stem into the free air and bear flowers. When it grows above its support, it must sooner or later bend downwards until it finds another support.

Some of the Vanda tribe do not have long stems. Their internodes are short, and in some cases very short. An example is Aerides, a fairly common Malayan orchid often cultivated for its fragrant flowers. An Aerides plant grows on the main branches of a tree, and itself branches freely, forming a sort of bushy growth, often with pendulous branches, each branch

FIG. 9—(a) climbing stem of *Vanda*, bearing leaves, 2 roots and an inflorescence × ½; (b) *Phalaenopsis cornu-cervi* plant with two old inflorescences × ⅓; (c) *Taeniophyllum* plant; stem-tip covered with scale-leaves, two inflorescences, and many roots × ⅓.

continuing to grow indefinitely but rather slowly in length, and each bearing a root for every two or three inches of stem-length. A member of this tribe which has even shorter stems is Phalaenopsis (Fig. 9b). The very beautiful *Phalaenopsis amabilis*, with its large, almost round white petals, native in Borneo and Java, is one of the most prized of all orchids. A Phalaenopsis stem is very short; in an old plant it will not be more than a few inches long. This means that the internodes, between the base of one leaf and the next, are very short, and the plant bears few leaves at one time. But the habit of growth, with stem apex growing indefinitely, and roots borne all along the stem, still holds for these orchids.

The most remarkable example of all, which it is at first sight difficult to believe could belong to the same tribe, is the genus Taeniophyllum (Fig. 9c). There are at present seventeen known species of this genus in Malaya, but they are so small that most people would never notice them. Each plant consists of a very short stem (rarely as much as an inch long even in an old plant) which bears a number of flat or rounded green roots spreading on the bark of the tree around it. Unless one examines the plant with a lens, one cannot see the leaves. The leaves are tiny brown scales, and therefore cannot do the normal work of green leaves. In the axils of some of these leaves grow the short slender flower-stalks, each of which bears a succession of tiny flowers, one at a time. Taeniophyllum is evidently highly evolved, but its evolution has consisted in reduction.

The peculiar habit of the plants of the Vanda tribe, with their indefinite growth in length of each stem, is a blessing to the gardener because it makes the plants very easy to propagate. One has only to cut off the top of any stem, to such a length that at least one root is included on the cutting, and the cut portion will go on growing almost without a check. Some side-branches will grow from the remaining part of the stem, and these in turn may be used as cuttings. But in the case of orchids with the other habit of growth, one has to make a cutting of the basal part, which alone bears the roots, and from which alone new buds, to form new erect leafy shoots, will come; one cannot cut off the end of a pseudobulb as a cutting, as its end has ceased growth.

There is an exception to this last statement. Some orchids, like Arundina, do produce small branches on their old stems or pseudobulbs, and these branches bear roots at the base, and can be detached for propagation. Each in fact forms a new plant; it is not strictly a part of the branching habit of the old one. And it is still true to say that one cannot cut off the end of a leafy stem or pseudobulb of such an orchid for purposes of propagation; each leafy stem or pseudobulb is limited in its growth in length, and comes to a definite end. The Vanda tribe have managed to get rid of this limitation by using the device of producing roots throughout the length of every stem.

The structure of a Vanda plant is called *monopodial*; the structure of orchids which have a succession of stems of limited growth is called *sympodial*.

We conclude this chapter with a general comparison of dicotyledons and monocotyledons (excluding Dracaena and its relatives). In a dicotyledonous tree, both stems and roots increase continually in thickness owing to the activity of a cambium. The xylem and phloem tissues which are most active in conducting water and food are always those nearest the cambium—that is, they are always young; this is an important fact in the efficiency of the tree. Even to old age, it has throughout a layer of active young cells not far beneath the bark. This is the secret of its perennial youthful vigour.

In a palm tree, there is no cambium. The xylem and phloem formed when the trunk is one foot high must remain in active condition as long as the palm lives; the conducting tissues are not continuously renewed. This must be a serious limiting factor.

But in a ginger with a creeping underground rhizome, the youthful vigour is maintained by continual new growth of the rhizome, and new roots on that new growth. So the monocotyledon that maintains a prostrate stem, with close contact between new stem-tissues and new roots, renews its active conducting tissues continuously, but in a different way from the dicotyledonous trees.

A palm tree might maintain its youthful vigour in the same way, if it had a horizontal trunk, bearing roots throughout. Some palms at any rate are capable of producing roots along most of their trunk, as is shown by date palms when treated in a special way. In Egypt, date palms vary much in quality, and they are therefore propagated vegetatively. This can be done from suckers which arise at the base of an old trunk. But the old trunk itself may also be rejuvenated if a hole is bored into it (about ten feet from the top), a piece of wood placed in the hole, and the trunk at that level then covered with earth (as in a marcot of an ordinary garden shrub or tree). Owing to the stimulus of the wounding, and of the earth, the trunk forms roots, and when these are sufficiently advanced the trunk may be cut through below the roots and replanted. Such a palm trunk, if repeatedly so treated, is potentially immortal, as is the rhizome of a ginger.

CHAPTER FOUR

YAMS AND SOME OTHER TUBERS

THE word yam is used very loosely by some people to cover any edible tuber that is not known to the speaker by any other distinctive name. In Malaya, it is often used by English-speaking people for the larger kinds of Kĕladi. True yams are distinctive in their slender climbing leafy stems; they have underground tubers of various kinds.

The collective botanical name for yams is Dioscorea, which commemorates the Greek physician Dioscorides, who wrote one of the most important classical works on medicinal plants. Yams are found in all tropical countries. They were first known to Europeans in West Africa, where Portuguese sailors took them for food on the homeward voyage, and the word yam seems to be a corruption of a Portuguese name for them. In Malaya, there are a number of wild yams, native in the forest (or more commonly on the borders of clearings), some of them eaten by the forest peoples and some poisonous; there are also a number of kinds of yam which are cultivated and not known in a truly wild condition. In Britain, the yam family is represented by the Black Bryony, common in hedgerows, known for its poisonous berries; its tuber is tough and inedible. In this chapter we will deal with some of the Malayan yams, and also with some other tubers, mainly from the point of view of habit of growth.

Yams are the most important native edible tubers in Malaya. The word *ubi* properly applies to the greater yam, called by botanists *Dioscorea alata*; the cultivation of this yam, in its many local races, extends from Madagascar to the Pacific, and the cognate names *ovi* in Madagascar and *ufi* in Tahiti are a remarkable relic of the travels of these plants in ancient times. Yams were used to provision sailing ships because they can be stored for a considerable time without deterioration.

The greater yam is only known in cultivation. It probably

originated in the region of Burma and Indo-China, where the long dry seasons are a stimulus to the formation of underground tubers, containing a store of food which can be used by the plant for its new growth when the next wet season begins. The native Malayan yams, formed in a country where dry seasons are short, are all less productive, and as one travels south in Malaya, the lack of seasonal change is also reflected in a reduction of the number of kinds of wild yams. But to return to the name ubi. This word is also used by Malays to describe tubers in general, and with an adjective to indicate a particular kind of tuber. Thus it has become applied to tapioca (ubi kayu) and sweet potatoes (ubi kĕledek), both of tropical American origin. These immigrant plants are both much less trouble to cultivate than the greater yam, and if you want to find a yam in a market in Singapore today you may have to look for some time before you find it.

Yams are monocotyledons; their stems do not increase in thickness as they grow older. The stems are slender, and they climb by means of twining round the stems of woody plants (Fig. 10*a*). Each yam stem grows from a tuberous base, and it takes food from the tuber during its early stages of growth. As the stem becomes older, its leaves manufacture an excess of food beyond that needed for the further growth of the stem itself, and this food is conducted downwards and stored in a new tuber (or tubers) which grows at the base of the stem (Fig. 10*a*¹). After about ten months the growth of the new tubers is complete. The climbing stems have done their job and they die. Normally, they should flower and bear fruit in the later stages of their growth, but in Singapore they often fail to flower. If now you dig up the tuber, and keep it in a dry airy place, it will rest for some time, but sooner or later you will see one or more buds beginning to grow from its upper end (the end nearest the stem which produced it). Now you can cut off part of the yam which bears the growing buds, and plant it, and eat the rest of the yam. Or if you keep the rest of it, this also will later produce some growing buds. If a yam is cut into a number of pieces, those near the top begin to grow first, and those from the bottom last.

Now let us look at the newly planted top of the yam. If it

FIG. 10—(*a*) *Dioscorea bulbifera:* twining stem × ¼; (*a¹*) base of stem and tuber × ¼; (*a²*) sprouting bulbil × ½; (*b*) young bulbil developing on *Dioscorea sansibarensis*; (*c*) ripe fruits of a yam × ½; (*c¹*) single seed from *c* × ¾.

is a large tuber, the bud will be large, and so the stem also. A yam bud, once it begins to grow, grows rapidly; it does not behave like the base of a palm trunk and consolidate its position before elongating; its position is, in fact, consolidated by the tuber from which it springs, and its size is limited by that tuber. The stem then grows rapidly upwards, and after a few days it will be growing several inches in a day. I once saw the new stem of a big African yam grow two feet in a day. At this stage the stem does little to develop its leaves; these remain small, and the lower ones never develop fully. After a week or two the leaves begin to develop, and the speed of growth of the stem diminishes somewhat. The stem, having no cambium, cannot increase in thickness after it is once formed, and the diameter of the stem limits both the amount of water that can go up within it, and the amount of manufactured food that can go down. Thus the size of the original bud determines the size of the plant, and the size of the new tuber it can form (sometimes a second bud may develop). There is a bud in the axil of each leaf of the climbing stem. A few of these buds may later grow to form branches of the yam, but most of them remain dormant. If the top of the stem is broken or damaged, a bud from the axil of a leaf near the top will make a new leader for the stem.

As soon as the stem begins to grow upwards, it also begins rapidly to form a number of thick roots at its base. These roots grow horizontally, and (like all roots) they gather water and salts from the soil for the growing stem. It is only when these roots are well developed that the new stem can carry a number of leaves, which are losing water all the time by evaporation. In some yams these roots have spiny branches, which help to protect the tubers from pigs and other animals. The tubers grow downwards (sometimes obliquely) beneath the roots. In the case of wild edible yams, the tubers go very deep, being borne on slender stalks, and in this way they are protected from animals. The yams which are poisonous have no need of this protection and are produced near the surface. The number of kinds of tuber formed by yams, both wild and cultivated, is very large. The range of form is probably greater than that of any other group of tubers.

Yam tubers appear to be of the nature of stems, not roots,

though on account of their peculiar structure there has been controversy on this point. The other tubers we shall consider are clearly either stems or roots.

But before leaving the yam, let us consider its seed and seedling. The fruit (produced from a tiny flower) is dry, three-winged, perhaps an inch long (Fig. 10c), breaking open to liberate seeds which are like round pieces of very thin smooth brown paper, each with a thicker part in the middle (Fig. 10c¹). The thicker part is the seed proper; the rest is a "wing" which helps the wind to disperse the seed.

The embryo in this small seed behaves very much like the embryo of a coconut, but on a much smaller scale. It has one cotyledon, the end of which remains in the seed to absorb the seed's food-store. The root grows down, the stem does not increase rapidly in length but bears a few leaves. Very soon the first root, which cannot increase in thickness, is inadequate and more roots grow from the stem. Part of the stem becomes thicker and forms the first tuber, and the tuber has a bud on it which can grow into another stem. After a time the leaves and roots die, leaving the small tuber. The tuber rests for a time, and then grows a new stem, larger than the seedling-stem because the tuber has a larger food supply than the seed, and so eventually the stem forms a larger tuber. The process is repeated until after perhaps three or more years a plant and tubers of full size are formed.

Several kinds of wild yams, and also one cultivated kind, pro-duce tubers in the axils of their leaves; a bud which normally would grow into a branch becomes a tuber. These aerial tubers are usually small, and they are called bulbils (Fig. 10a²). The cultivated plant which bears them (sometimes called by the Malay name ubi atas) has bulbils as big as good-sized potatoes, which are edible, though in my opinion not as good as the earth-tubers of the greater yam.

A poisonous African yam called *Dioscorea sansibarensis* has become established as a weed in Singapore. It was introduced for experimental purposes in the Botanic Gardens, and has spread by means of its bulbils. It has never produced seeds. It provides an interesting example of the effort a plant can make to propagate itself. If you cut off a yard or so of the leafy stem

E

of this yam, and let it hang or lie in an airy but shaded place, it withers very slowly. You will not notice much change for a week or ten days. Then as the leaves wither you will see that the buds in the axils of one or more leaves begin to swell, and by the end of about three weeks these buds will have grown into bulbils (Fig. 10*b*). By this time the stem and leaves will have completely shrivelled and died; but before dying the stem has concentrated its substance in one or two bulbils which will live and grow to produce new (though small) plants. So if you think to kill this yam by cutting off its stems near the ground, those stems (unless you remove and destroy them) will form a quantity of tubers which will later fall to the ground, and ultimately you will have many plants in place of one.

It seems that some yams (like this African yam) have a tuber which grows larger and larger every year. Its substance is not used up by the growth of the leafy stem, but only temporarily diminished; the full-grown leafy stem returns to the tuber all and more than all it took when it was young, so that the tuber becomes larger and larger every year. This is not, however, true of the commonly cultivated edible yams.

In countries with a fairly long dry season, yams are planted (or if wild begin to grow) with the new rains. and the leafy stems die in the dry season. In Singapore you can plant a yam tuber any time its new shoot happens to begin growth, at any time of the year, and when the new tubers are fully grown the leafy stems will die. The new tubers then rest for a time, especially if dug up and dried. Nobody has observed the natural growth-period of wild yams in Singapore, but I should be surprised if they correspond exactly in the same way to the calendar every year, though yams no doubt do this in the north of Malaya.

Now we will consider the case of tapioca, or ubi kayu. The usual way to plant tapioca is to cut a stem into lengths of nine inches or so, and half-bury them in the ground. The buried part of the cutting soon produces roots, and the top produces one or more leafy shoots. The leafy shoots grow gradually into woody stems which increase in thickness by the activity of a cambium, just as the trunk of a tree does. The roots also become gradually thicker by the activity of cambium, but in their case the xylem formed contains at first very little woody tissue; it consists chiefly of living cells containing starch. The roots in fact become food-storing tubers. When the roots are big enough we can dig them up and eat them. As many people in Malaya have good reason to know, they contain little besides starch, and are not by themselves good food, as a yam or potato is; they must be sufficiently supplemented with food containing proteins and vitamins.

If you let a tapioca plant go on growing for eighteen months or so, it becomes almost a tree, and its roots then are very large. At this stage the roots also become too woody to eat as a vegetable, for which reason they are called ubi kayu. They are used at this stage for the extraction of starch, which is washed and dried and is the tapioca of commerce. Not all kinds of ubi kayu will go on growing for more than a year; the kinds commonly planted produce useful starchy roots in about six months (or even less) and are then dug up. If they are not dug, the leafy parts of the stem become thin and poor, and it seems that the plant eventually dies. But it is difficult to get precise information on this simple matter.

The tuber of ubi kayu is a root. If you cut off such a tuber and bury it in the ground, it will remain sound for a long time (some months at least), but it will not produce a leafy stem. The tuber in fact is not an organ of propagation, as a yam is. What good then is the tuber to the tapioca plant? I have never seen an answer to this question, and can only guess. Perhaps one could find the answer experimentally.

Tapioca comes from tropical America, where it was widely cultivated at the time of Columbus. It was brought to Asia by Europeans, but not until towards the end of the eighteenth century. The tubers do not keep well, and they cannot be used for propagation, for which reasons tapioca was not such an early traveller as the good kinds of yam. Presumably if one wants to know what use the tubers are to the plant, one must go to the American tropics and study wild tapioca, or its nearest relatives. Tapioca plants have a woody stem; they are not like the biennial plants of Europe (such as the carrot) which store food in a root, after which the green leafy stem dies to the ground for the following winter. But the plants probably have to live through a dry season, and it may be that the tubers are primarily water-stores rather than food-stores. It may also be that races with big starchy tubers have been selected by man, and are not found in wild plants.

Tapioca plants in Malaya do not often flower, perhaps because they are always dug before the flowering stage. It may be that in their own country they flower in dry weather, when the leaves have mostly fallen, and that the tubers play some part in the flowering and fruiting.

We turn now to the other edible tuber which comes from tropical America, the sweet potato, or ubi kĕledek. This also is planted from cuttings. The usual procedure is to plant the green tips of the leafy stems, or sometimes older portions of stems, in a ridge of earth. The cuttings become very limp when exposed to the full sun in an unrooted condition, but roots begin to grow in a few days, and the limp leaves revive. The roots are adventitious, produced by the part of the stem-cutting which is in the ground; the stems are slender, and trail over the ground, rooting at intervals if they are allowed to do so. It is usual to move the stems frequently to prevent such rooting, as this may check the growth of the first roots formed by the original cutting. These original roots, after attaining a certain length, grow in thickness, and after three to five months (according to variety) they have reached their full size. The leaves then begin to wither, and it is time to dig the root-tubers. As in tapioca, the secondary thickening, formed by cambium, consists mainly of food-storage tissue.

We can now take the ends of the trailing stems, and plant them as cuttings for a new crop. There is no planting season in Malaya, except possibly in the north; you can plant sweet potatoes at any time.

Sweet potatoes cannot be stored long; that is one of their disadvantages in a place where there is only one growing season in the year, but in Malaya it is of no great consequence. If you keep a sweet potato on a shelf for three or four weeks, you may find that it produces buds which will grow into leafy stems. In this it differs from tapioca roots, which are incapable of producing such buds, as are roots of most other kinds of plants. It seems therefore that, from the plant's point of view, sweet potatoes are resting organs which store food during a dry (or perhaps a cool) season, and can later produce new stems to continue the growth of the plant. It seems also that they are not adapted to rest over a very long period.

Sweet potato plants flower occasionally in Malaya, but I have never seen any seeds, and therefore no seedlings. The flowers are usually self-sterile; they need pollination from flowers of another variety if they are to produce seeds. Such pollination, carried out artificially, can be used to produce new kinds of sweet potatoes (see Chapter 6).

In Chapter 2, discussing the differences between a dicotyledon (the Rubber tree) and a monocotyledon (the Coconut palm) we noted that the dicotyledon had a main root which increased in size, and that the other roots were branches of it, whereas in the palm, new small roots were continually produced from the base of the stem. In both tapioca and sweet potato, we plant pieces of stem, and they bear roots, in the same way that monocotyledons do. Most dicotyledon stems have the power of producing roots if necessary; the difference from monocotyledons is that these stem-borne roots (which are called adventitious) can increase in thickness, whereas those on a monocotyledon cannot.

Next we come to true potatoes. Unlike a sweet potato, a true potato has "eyes", and each eye has an eyebrow. The eyes are buds, and the eyebrows are rudimentary leaves. The potato is, in fact, a specially thickened part of an underground stem, not a root. Its secondary thickening is almost all occupied by a food-store. It is really something like a yam in its nature, being a stem, but it is a dicotyledon. The potato tuber can increase in thickness by a cambium. When you plant a part of a tuber, with an eye in it, the leafy stem is not limited by the size of the eye, as a yam stem is, but can also increase in thickness. The potato is a resting storage organ, just as a yam is, and it tides the plant over from one growing season to the next. In the lowlands of Malaya, potatoes will not grow vigorously, but they can be grown at hill stations. They may be planted at any time of year, and harvested when the tubers are fully grown.

A këladi is the thick erect stem of a monocotyledon (Fig. 11a). It may be compared to the trunk of a palm, but the këladi stem never grows more than a short distance above the ground, and it is not woody. Kĕladi leaves are large, but not so large as palm leaves, and quite different in shape.

If you buy a kĕladi in the market, you will see it to be a cylindrical object with rings round it, and at one end is a bud. The rings are the marks of leaf-bases, just as they are on a palm trunk. But in a kĕladi the bud in the axil of any leaf may grow into a new stem. So if you cut the kĕladi into several parts by transverse cuts, and plant the parts, a bud on each will grow and produce a new kĕladi. When it begins to grow, the bud behaves like the stem of a palm seedling; it increases its width before increasing much in height. As with a palm, during the process of increase of width, a succession of larger and larger leaves are formed until the full size is produced. Each leaf has a fairly thick fleshy stalk, and a more or less triangular blade; the stalk is not attached at the edge of the blade. The stem or tuber of the kĕladi goes on growing until it reaches the surface on the ground; if you then add more earth, it will grow taller. Otherwise, probably some of the lateral buds will grow and produce more stems.

There are a great many varieties of keladi, and they show some differences in behaviour. The kind most grown for the market, which gives the best yield of edible tuber, is called kĕladi china (because it is the kind most grown by Chinese). In places where there is a dry season, this kĕladi ceases to grow during the drought, and is then harvested, but in the south of Malaya there does not seem to be any natural check to growth due to dry weather. Keladi china gives a single large tuber. Other kinds are more prone to branching, and will give several smaller ones. Yet others never produce a good thick fleshy stem, but they produce many juicy, slender horizontal underground side-branches, which are eaten as a vegetable. The young leaves of some kinds of kĕladi are also used as a green vegetable.

Kĕladis are of Asiatic origin, and they were known in the eastern Mediterranean two thousand years ago; the genus bears the ancient name Colocasia. In tropical America an allied genus of plants has developed, called Xanthosoma by botanists, or Yautia (Fig. 11b). A few kinds of Yautia are grown in Malaya. They are usually called kĕladi bĕtawi or keladi sarawak, or some such name which indicates a foreign origin. The leaves are

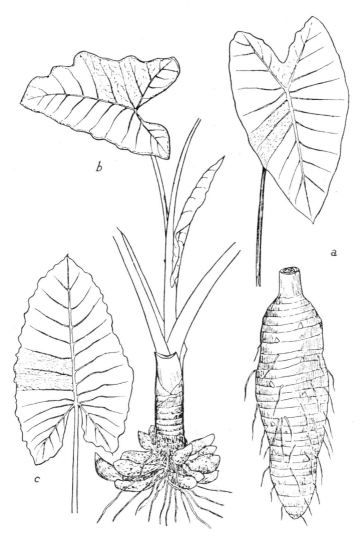

Fig. 11—(a) *Kĕladi China:* tuberous stem, and leaf × ¼; (b) *Yautia* plant × ⅛; (c) leaf of *Alocasia* × ⅛.

larger than those of any kĕladi, and the blade is cut down to the insertion of the leaf-stalk. The growing plants look much like kĕladis, but the erect underground stems bear many side-tubers, which are of uneven shape, about as big as an average potato. These side-tubers are the edible parts. Like potatoes, they have eyes and can be used for propagation. There is a third genus of the same family, called Alocasia; the Malayan name for this is Bira (Fig. 11c). This has thick, erect starchy stems like a kĕladi but they commonly grow a foot or more above the ground. The leaves of well-grown plants are very large, and may easily be recognized by the raised main veins on their upper surface. Bira stems are not edible, because they contain abundant large needle-shaped crystals of calcium oxalate, which cause severe irritation of the mouth.

Kĕladis also have such crystals, but they are smaller, and when the kĕladi is cooked the crystals are no longer a serious irritant, though sometimes their presence may be slightly felt. Raw kĕladis, and their raw leaves, are, however, just as unpleasant to eat as the cooked stem of Bira. The reason is interesting, and known to few people. The needle-shaped crystals in a kĕladi are in close bundles packed in special cylindrical cells. If the end of one such cell is broken, the pressure of the sap in the cell ejects the crystals forcibly, a few at a time, through the opening, as if the cell were hurling spears at its foe. This process can easily be seen under a microscope. It is this forcible ejection of the crystals that causes irritation of the mouth when one eats raw kĕladi. Now if you cook the kĕladi, the cells are killed, and the forcible ejection is no longer possible. Furthermore, the protoplasm surrounding the bundle of fibres is solidified, and forms a sort of gelatinous blanket to the whole bundle. But in the case of Bira, the crystals are so much larger and stronger that cooking does not destroy their effect.

Kĕladi, Yautia, and Bira have very peculiar flowers, somewhat like those of the well-known white "Arum Lily", which is cultivated at Cameron Highlands. There is a leafy sheath, white in the arum, greenish in kĕladis and their near allies; from the funnel-shaped base of this sheath emerges a spike. The spike is entirely covered with very small flowers, which may develop later into red berry-like fruits. The fruits contain seeds, which will grow into new plants; but as in the case of the other tubers mentioned in this chapter, kĕladis are not usually propagated by seeds. It is quicker and easier to grow them from cuttings of old tubers.

All these tuberous plants, each in its particular way and with the particular limitations of its inner structure, produce a store of food underground, and (except tapioca) a bud or buds which make use of that food-store in beginning the next season's growth. Such tubers are especially characteristic of regions with a pronounced dry season, in which growth is impossible. Those of Asiatic origin have doubtless mainly developed in the regions immediately north of Malaya, where there is a monsoon climate. In the north of Malaya there is enough dry season to keep them to their periods of growth and rest, but in much of Malaya this is not so. We use these plants because they have developed convenient stores of food; this development took place mainly in another climate, but the plants continue their food-storing habits in this country though they really need not do so.

CHAPTER FIVE

VEGETATIVE PROPAGATION

IN the preceding three chapters, there have been various indications that tubers, rhizomes, and other parts of a plant may be used for purposes of propagation; that is, for making new plants. Such new plants are grown from pieces of an old plant, and they are actually parts of the old plant. The process of growing a new plant from part of an old one is called vegetative propagation. It is quite different from propagation by seeds, which we will consider in the next chapter.

If part of a plant is to be used to produce a whole new plant, that part must be able to produce all the organs of a complete plant, namely, roots, stems, leaves, and flowers. If the part used is a stem, the stem must be able to grow roots, and also it must have a bud or buds which can grow into leafy stems. If the part used is a root, it must be able to develop buds which will form leafy stems (we saw that the sweet potato root will do this). In some cases it is possible to propagate a plant from a leaf; in that case, the leaf must be able to produce both stem and roots.

Another consideration is that the part used for propagation must have a store of food in it, to give the new plant a start in life, just as a seed does. It is true that the store may in some cases be small, but it must be present.

The underground resting tubers of yams are nature's own method of vegetative propagation. If undisturbed, they produce what in fact are new plants year after year. By digging up a yam, cutting the tuber into pieces, and planting them in different places, man merely enlarges the scope of a normal natural process.

In the same way the rhizome of a ginger or a Canna, which we noted as being potentially immortal, may be dug up, divided, and the pieces planted elsewhere. The rhizome already bears

58

roots, rudimentary leaves, and buds. It is not a resting organ like a yam tuber, and is ready to start new growth as soon as it is planted. The climbing stem of a Vanda, which produces new roots at intervals all along its length, may be cut into pieces, each bearing a few roots and several leaves, and each piece will grow. These monocotyledons which root freely on their creeping or climbing stems are, in fact, very easy to propagate vegetatively. Their whole structure is adapted to the purpose.

As we saw in Chapter 2, a Rubber tree is quite different in its way of growth. It has a branching root-system entirely below the ground, and a branching stem entirely above the ground, and the two are quite separate. The stem does not produce roots, nor do the roots produce stem-buds. Most trees are like that.

But as we all know, it is possible to grow many plants from cuttings, which are parts of stems. Such stem-cuttings of dicotyledons have the power of producing roots, just as do the stems of monocotyledons. In the stem is a store of food (mostly in the xylem) which is sufficient to provide for the growth of roots and new leafy shoots. One might think that the stems of trees in Malaya would not need to store food, as their leaves are making new food every day in the year. But many evergreen trees do not grow new leafy twigs continuously; growth is usually in sudden flushes, and this is always true of deciduous trees. A store of food is needed to provide for these flushes of rapid growth. The same store can be used to provide for the growth of roots and buds on a cutting. (It should be remembered that though growth of new leafy twigs is not continuous, the activity of cambium in an evergreen tree is continuous, and takes some of the food made by the leaves.)

In most cases, we take a cutting of a twig which has become woody, and therefore has a store of food. We remove most of the leaves from the cutting, because leaves lose water all the time, and a cutting without roots cannot absorb much water from the soil. The chief danger for an unrooted cutting is that it may become dry before it has produced new roots; to maintain the processes of its life, it must have a sufficient water-content. So it is usually necessary to shelter such a cutting from the heat of the sun. The cutting is placed in sandy soil, which is kept moist, so that roots, when they grow, may have suitable conditions. A rich soil is undesirable, because a rich soil encourages the growth of many kinds of fungi and bacteria, and some of these may attack the cutting in its vulnerable unrooted condition, and kill it before it can produce roots.

It happens that some plants are best propagated from quite green cuttings, taken from the growing tips of the twigs. It is evident that these are more vulnerable to loss of water than are older woody cuttings, and they must be more completely protected. If such green cuttings are to be useful, they must root quickly. In some cases (for example, Oleander and Coleus) it is possible to place them in water, and they will produce roots in the water; the base of the stem can absorb enough water to keep the leaves from withering. When the roots are formed, the cuttings can be potted in earth; but the new roots are very fragile, and must be handled with great care. In other cases, cuttings root well in a layer of moist sawdust or coir dust; these substances hold both moisture and air. If the cuttings in their rooting medium are covered with a glass bell-jar, or placed in a box with a piece of glass on the top, excessive loss of water is prevented. If such cuttings do not form roots quickly, they may rot, owing to the entry of harmful organisms. However, in some cases it is possible to keep green leafy cuttings alive for three or four months, after which they may produce roots. It is possible to accelerate root formation by means of substances called growth hormones, which are sold commercially. But it usually happens that these hormones are of little or no use in the case of cuttings which are very slow, or which normally do not produce any roots.

There are some plants of which stem cuttings will not produce roots, or will produce them so rarely that propagation by cuttings is not practicable on a large scale. The Rubber tree is one such plant. We then have to resort to other methods. One method which is often used, though it is a little laborious, is called *marcotting*. Rambutans and Chiku trees are often propagated by this method; also various garden shrubs.

If you take a knife and cut through the bark of a branch, down to the cambium, making a complete ring round the branch, then make another ring a short distance away, and remove all the bark between the rings, you have completely severed the connection between the phloem of the branch above the cut and the phloem below the cut. Then, though water can pass up from the roots to the leaves on that branch, food made by the leaves cannot pass downwards beyond the ring. The result is a congestion of food above the ring, and this has a stimulating effect on the tissues near the upper cut, which is soon healed by a callus tissue formed by the cambium. But if you cover the bare ring of wood with earth, tie the earth in place (this is done with coconut husk), and keep the earth moist, roots will usually grow from the stem near the upper cut. When the roots are strong enough, you can cut off the branch below the ring, and plant it. It is sometimes possible to marcot a fairly large branch, still carrying all its leaves, and the result is a larger plant than could be obtained from a cutting.

Ringing of the bark in the way above described, or merely constriction of the bark by means of a tight band of wire, may sometimes result in another response to the stopping of phloem food-channels. The accumulation of food may induce flowering (and so fruiting) on the branch. The wiring method (which does not involve the complete destruction of a ring of bark, and so does little harm to the tree) is sometimes used to induce flowering in Citrus trees, but little experiment on this matter has been done in Malaya.

Everybody who reads the newspapers knows that Rubber trees are budded, and we have referred to this process in our comparison of a Rubber tree and a Coconut palm in Chapter 2. If cuttings of Rubber trees rooted easily, we should not need to bud them. There is no magic in the budding process; it is only a more ingenious device of vegetative propagation applied to a difficult subject. It has also some other advantages, as we shall see.

The reason why Rubber trees are bud-grafted is that trees grown from seeds vary in the amount of rubber they will yield. If we could grow cuttings from a high-yielding tree, all trees grown from such cuttings would have the same high yield. We cannot grow cuttings, and so buds are taken from the high-yielding tree, and each bud is attached to a rooted plant grown from a seed. The bud grows, and the final result is a high-yielding tree growing on roots which are not its own. The same process of budding can also be used for propagating Rambutans and other fruit trees. Rambutans can be marcotted, but budding is less laborious and it is economical in material of the mother tree (only one bud is needed for each new plant). The purpose of budding fruit trees is again to propagate good varieties; in this case, trees which bear fruit of fine quality, and also trees which flower and therefore fruit freely in the climatic conditions in which they are to be grown. For example, trees of some kinds of Avocado pear produce much better crops of fruit than other kinds in Singapore.

The essentials of bud-grafting have been mentioned in Chapter 2. Here we will deal in more detail with the method used for budding Rubber. Seedling Rubber trees which are to be used as stocks for budding are grown in nursery beds until they are of a suitable thickness. It is essential that these seedlings should be growing vigorously, with an active cambium, so that the bark may be peeled off easily. Buds are taken from a small woody branch of the selected mother tree (not from a young leaf-bearing twig). This branch is cut off and brought to the nursery where budding is to be done. The bud has to be placed on the stock near the ground, as the tappable trunk of the resulting tree must be provided by the high-yielding scion. A horizontal cut is made in the stock, down to the cambium layer, and a vertical cut downwards at each end of the horizontal one. Then we have cuts down to the cambium along three sides of a rectangle. The outer tissues are next separated by pulling the free top of the rectangle downwards; if the seedling is in active growth the delicate cells around the cambium will break down and the operation will be easy. The cambium is then exposed. The stripped portion of bark is then cut off near the base. Next a bud is cut from the branch of the mother tree, and with the bud a slice of bark down to cambium level. The bark is trimmed to fit the rectangle exposed on the seedling stock, and the two cambiums (of stock and bud) are placed carefully in contact. The base of the bud-patch will be held in position by the remaining bottom part of the flap of bark of the stock. The bud and its patch of bark are then tied firmly in position, and protected from the sun's heat by a bunch of leaves. If the operation has been done successfully, the two cambiums should unite, and the bud and its patch of bark will then become part of the stock. The whole operation must be done quickly and accurately, so that the delicate cambiums of stock and bud are exposed for the minimum of time and are not injured in any way by touching or rubbing.

When the union has taken place, the top of the seedling is cut off, and the bud begins to grow. Only the stem produced by this bud (called the scion) is allowed to grow upwards. The scion is then completely united with the stock, and in due time we have a tree with trunk and branches formed by the scion, and root-system formed by the stock.

As we have already noted, there is a variation among Rubber seedlings in yield of latex; there is much variation also in vigour of growth and in many characters of habit, leaf-shape, bark, etc. Therefore, though the scions of budded Rubber all come from one mother tree and are alike in all characters, the stocks are variable, having been grown from different seeds. The junction between scion and stock in a Rubber tree can often be seen, and sometimes there is a marked difference in appearance between the two. In the case of Apple trees in England, it has been shown that the stocl has a considerable influence on the development and behaviour (both as regards fruiting and also vigour of growth) of the scion. By ingenious methods, stocks have been propagated vegetatively, and so uniformity both of stock and scion is possible; and a series of different stocks has been standardized, so that for every scion a series of different and standardized reactions is possible. This has not yet been achieved for Para rubber, and it seems doubtful whether it would be worth doing even if it were practicable, as the demonstrated effects of stock on scion in this case are less than in Apple trees. But I think that in the case of fruit trees in Malaya the stock-scion interrelationships may well become important when we have more varieties of fruits to propagate. That will have to wait for further work in breeding (see Chapter 6).

Another method of propagation, akin to budding, is grafting. In this process a small branch of the scion, with a growing tip, is fastened to a branch of similar size on the stock. Again, the essence of the process is a union of the cambiums of stock and scion. The ends to be united are cut in various ways so as to ensure a firm union, and in most cases the cuts are oblique so as to give a greater length of contact between the two cambiums. Again, the cutting and fitting of stock and scion must be quickly, neatly, and accurately done, with a minimum of touching and rubbing which might damage the delicate cambium. The scion, which is a leafy twig with a growing tip, is much more vulnerable to drying than a bud which has no expanded leaves. The grafted scion, therefore, needs shelter from the sun and wind until union is made. In this case there is no need to cut off the top of the stock; it is cut off before the scion is attached.

An interesting case in which grafting of this kind may be used is the Tomato. Tomatoes suffer much from a bacterial wilt disease of the roots. The organism causing this disease is present in most old garden soils, and if it is present, Tomato plants nearly always die about the time they begin to flower. The bacteria enter the roots and finally choke the water-channels of the stems, so that the leaves die from lack of water.

One way to overcome this disease is to sterilize the soil, and this in practice means growing your Tomato plants in large pots or old kerosene tins, because it is nearly impossible to sterilize all the soil in a garden bed. But another method is also possible. There are plants related to the Tomato, upon which Tomato scions can be grafted, which have roots not attacked by the wilt disease. These related plants are the various kinds of Těrong —the cultivated Brinjal, and its wild relatives. Tomatoes may be grafted on to the ordinary cultivated Těrong, but this does not seem vigorous enough. Experiments in Java, just before the war, showed that Těrong Pipit (*Solanum torvum*), which has quite small fruits, is the best stock on which to graft Tomatoes. Singapore experiments have been less successful, but there is no doubt that further trials would indicate a suitable stock. The procedure is not difficult. One has to raise a stock of seedlings of Těrong and also of Tomatoes. In practice, the young Tomato plants grow quicker and so should be planted later. When the Těrong seedlings are big enough, tops of Tomato seedlings can be grafted on them. If the grafting is correctly done, the union is made in a few days and the Tomato plant then grows on the roots of the Těrong.

The garden varieties of Hibiscus may also be propagated by budding or grafting. There may be two reasons for doing this. Some kinds of Hibiscus (especially those with yellow flowers) are much less vigorous in growth than others. If a cutting of a strong growing kind is rooted, and then a scion of one of the weaker kinds is grafted or budded on it, the scion grows more strongly than on its own roots. The other reason why budding may be practised is for the production of "standard" plants; that is, plants with a tall bare stem and a group of branches at the top of it. The procedure is to root a long straight cutting and then bud or graft the scion to the top of it. The scion only is then allowed to produce leafy and flowering branches. By this method it is obviously possible, by grafting several scions, to produce a bush with several different kinds of flowers.

Budding and grafting may be applied to many kinds of dicotyledons, and are used in most cases where vegetative propagation of trees is necessary to ensure a uniformly high-quality plantation. In some cases budding on to seedling stocks may have the advantage of giving a better-developed root-system than a cutting can develop, because a seedling produces a primary or tap root and a cutting cannot. Budding and grafting require skill, but given this skill they are economical of material and time.

Next we come to leaf-cuttings. A leaf normally has no power of further development after it is once formed. When it is old, it is shed, as being of no more use to the plant. Its function is to manufacture food which can be used by the growing parts of the plant, but it makes no further growth itself. There are a few exceptions to this rule, and one of them is a plant which is sometimes found in gardens in Malaya, and sometimes runs wild in sandy ground. This is Bryophyllum, the "life-plant", so called because the old leaves produce a number of small buds along their edges, and each bud can grow into a new plant. So every old leaf that falls need not die, but can produce more plants. There are also a few other cultivated plants of the same family (mainly African) which behave in the same way.

There are some other plants which do not normally produce buds on their leaves but can be induced to do so. If you take a leaf of one of the large-leaved Begonias, cut through the main

F

veins with a razor in a few places, and then place the leaf flat on the surface of sand which is kept moist, buds will grow at some of the cuts, and each bud can form a new Begonia plant, with stem, leaves, and roots.

If you take a leaf of Saintpaulia (the African Violet) complete with its stalk, and plunge the stalk in sand or sawdust, which is kept moist, a bud will form on the buried stalk. Some other kinds of plants have also been propagated in this way, and perhaps a good many could be so if we knew exactly how to treat them; but in most cases leaves will not readily form buds, which is not surprising in view of the specialized nature of leaves.

Finally, we have root cuttings. A root has from the first a different anatomical structure from a stem, and roots do not normally transform themselves into stems. But in some cases roots can form buds which have stem structure and can bear leaves. Sometimes you will see "suckers" coming up from the ground around an old tree or shrub (not to be confused with seedlings grown from fallen seeds). These suckers have grown from buds on the main roots. Sometimes injury to a root will cause such budding. The common orange-flowered Ixora, much grown in Malayan gardens, will form root suckers. There is an Australian Casuarina (*C. glauca*), sometimes planted in Singapore, which forms abundant root-suckers, sometimes far from the trunk of the parent tree.

Root cuttings may be used in some cases for propagation in place of stem cuttings. An example is the Breadfruit tree, which is usually propagated from rather thick root cuttings. It cannot be propagated from seeds, as the fruits contain no seeds. Roots may also be used for grafting, but I know of no experiments on this in Malaya.

CHAPTER SIX

FLOWERS AND HYBRIDS

EVERYONE knows that flowers normally result in the formation of seeds. Except in certain plants which are uncommon in Malaya, seeds are produced inside fruits. A bean pod is a fruit containing seeds. Some fruits are small or hard, or otherwise unlike the edible fruits to which we commonly attach this term. But nevertheless they are fruits, formed from the same part of the flower as the fruits we eat. Nature has produced an enormous diversity of flowers, and we in Malaya have a much larger number of them than most countries. Every flower produces its own peculiar kind of fruit, and each fruit contains one or more seeds.

Two questions now arise, which we shall discuss in the present chapter. The first question is, what are the parts of a flower, and how do they form a fruit and seeds? The second question is, why should the plant go to so much trouble to produce seeds, when a much simpler method of propagation seems possible? For example, there are several kinds of yams which have little tubers on their climbing stems. When they are fullgrown (usually an inch or so across) the tubers fall, and then they can rest and later produce new plants, just as seeds do. But the yams also produce seeds, which would seem to serve the same purpose. The production of seeds involves the whole complex mechanism of flowering, as we shall see. Why then should not all plants cut out this complication, and be content with producing little tubers, as the yams do? This is a very fundamental question, and we shall only be able to indicate the nature of the answer.

As an example of a flower, we will take the common orchid Vanda Miss Joaquim (Fig. 12a). This flower has the peculiar structure of all orchids, and we will consider later another flower of more normal structure. The value of the Vanda as an example

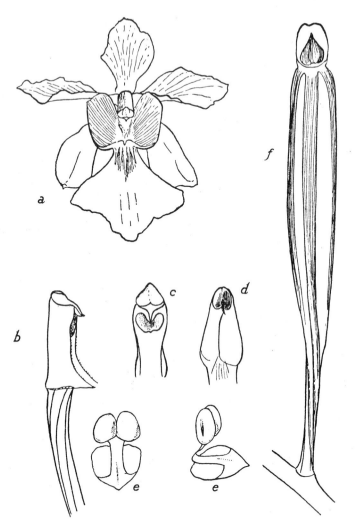

Fig. 12—*Vanda Miss Joaquim:* (*a*) flower × 1; (*b*) column and ovary × 2;
(*c*) front of column × 2; (*d*) column a few days after pollination × 2; (*e*) pollinia,
front and side views × 4; (*f*) a fully grown fruit × 1.

is that the parts are easy to see, and in this flower the process of pollination and its effects can also be clearly seen.

A flower of Vanda Miss Joaquim which is just opening can be seen to have three outer parts which quite cover the inner ones until the opening of the flower. These outer parts are called sepals; two of them have curious little tails near their tips. When the flower is fully open, one of the sepals stands at the top, and one spreads on each side, drooping a little. On each side of the top sepal is a petal. The petals are a little larger than the top sepal, and rounder; they are twisted at the base, so that the surface which should be at the back is turned towards you. Between the other two sepals, at the bottom of the flower, is a large structure called the *lip*. It is really the third petal, but it is more complicated in structure than the others. The lips of orchid flowers usually consist of three parts or *lobes*. In this case the middle lobe is much larger than the others, and is deep mauve. The side-lobes spread on each side of the base of the lip, and are flushed with orange and mauve. Where the three lobes meet there is a hollow, which is seen as a projection when the back of the flower is examined; this is the spur. The petals and sepals form the conspicuous part of the flower. Their duty is to attract visitors, which the flower needs if it is to fulfil its work of producing seeds.

In the middle of the flower is a curious more or less cylindrical projection called the *column*. At the back of the flower the end of the stalk, where this joins the flower, is angled and curiously twisted; the column is actually a continuation of this angled part (Fig. 12b). Now look at the top of the column (Fig. 12c). It is covered with a sort of cap, pointed towards the lip, and beneath the point is a hollow in the front of the column. Take a matchstick or similar splinter of wood and place the tip of the stick underneath the point of the cap at the top of the column; then press gently upwards, and wait a few seconds. Now remove the matchstick gently. You will find that the cap becomes detached, falling away, and that the end of your matchstick is stuck to a little disc of tissue which carries upon it two yellow blobs (Fig. 12e).

The yellow blobs consist of pollen. In most flowers, pollen is like yellow powder, but in orchids it is stuck together into small masses like this, and the masses (called *pollinia*) are always so arranged in relation to a sticky disc, or a bit of substance that is not a disc, that a suitable visiting insect is sure to carry them away, as they were carried away on the matchstick. The commonest insects visiting Vanda flowers are the large carpenter bees which make holes in old pieces of wood.

Now make the following experiment. Without picking a flower, remove its pollen, and then place the pollen in the hollow on the front of the column. The hollow is called the stigma. The interior of the stigma is sticky, and should retain the pollen mass easily. Next morning look at the flower. The petals and sepals have faded white; they have done their work, and need not make a show any longer. If you look at the column with a lens, you will see that it is swollen (Fig. 12*d*), and you may no longer be able to distinguish the mass of pollen. Now wait two weeks. The petals and sepals have withered and gone. The angled part of the stalk behind the flower has considerably swollen and grown longer. This part is in fact growing into a fruit. Wait about four months, and the fruit is ripe (Fig. 12*f*); it turns yellowish and then brown, splitting open along three double lines. Inside the fruit are a lot of twisted hairs and some fine red-brown dust. The particles of dust are seeds, and there are many thousands of them. The angled and twisted part of the stalk which grows into the fruit is really part of the flower itself; it is called the *ovary*. In this case the ovary is said to be inferior because it is below the attachment of the other floral parts; in many other flowers the ovary is superior, and can be seen in the middle of the flower. The ovary contains small organs which will later develop into seeds when the ovary itself becomes the fruit.

If you take another flower of the Vanda, and remove the pollen, without putting it into the hollow stigma on the front of the column, the whole flower merely withers. It does not form a fruit.

This is clear demonstration that if a fruit (containing seeds) is to be formed, the pollen must be put on to the stigma. This process is called pollination, and it is often done for the flower by visiting insects. I know of few other flowers in which the reaction to pollination can so clearly be seen.

With the unaided eye one can see the effects of pollination, but not the details of the behaviour of the pollen. When the pollen is placed upon the stigma, every one of its thousands of pollen grains begins to grow. Each grain forms a very fine tube, which penetrates to the middle of the column and grows down into the ovary. The swelling of the column is to accommodate all the pollen tubes. When a pollen tube reaches the hollow of the ovary, it meets a small object called an *ovule*, of which there are many in the ovary. In the ovule is a female reproductive cell. In the tube formed by the pollen grain is a male reproductive cell. The tube carries the male cell to the mouth of the ovule where the female cell is placed, and the two reproductive cells then unite within the ovule. The result is that the ovule begins to grow, ultimately forming a seed, and the united cell formed by the sexual fusion develops into the embryo within that seed. The act of pollination (pollen placed on the stigma), stimulates the ovary to grow into a fruit; seeds are formed as the result of the fusion of male cells (derived from pollen grains) with female cells (formed in the ovules). The embryo in the seed is not merely part of the plant which bears the seed; it is a new being, formed by a sexual process, and may (as we shall see) have a distinct individuality of its own.

A disadvantage of the orchid, for purposes of study, is that the seeds are very small, and one cannot easily see their development. We will now take another flower in which the process of seed-development is more easily followed. In one of the commonly cultivated beans the pollen is powdery and produced close to the stigma, so that the fact of pollination and its results are not easily demonstrated, but the development of fruit and seeds is easily followed. A convenient example is Kachang Kara, the Egyptian Kidney Bean (*Dolichos lablab*), which is commonly cultivated in Malaya. The plants are long-lived and flower continuously.

The flowers are produced in branched erect sprays (Fig. 13a). Such a spray of flowers (which in different plants may vary in its shape and method of branching) is called an inflorescence.

Each flower of Kachang Kara (Fig. 13a^1–a^4) has a green cup at the base; this cup is called the calyx, and it protects the inner parts of the flower when they are young as the sepals do in a

Vanda. The petals are white, and are not all alike. At the top of the flower a broad petal stands erect (Fig. 13a^2); it is called the standard. At its base are curious thickenings which grip some other parts of the flower and hold them in place. As you face the flower, a boat-shaped part points towards you, and on each side of this is a small white petal (Fig. 13a^3). If now you pull off (carefully) the standard and two side petals, you are left with the boat-shaped part (called the keel) which is covered with two more petals (Fig. 13a^4) partly joined together (you can see their bases are separate). Now pull off these petals, and you are left with the stamens and the ovary (Fig. 13a^5). In the bean flower there are ten stamens, each consisting of a small anther, containing powdery yellow pollen, on a very slender stalk. Nine of the stamens are joined to a boat-shaped sheath in which lies the ovary; the tenth stamen is quite free and attached separately at the base of the standard petal. Inside the stamen-sheath is a little sweet nectar (you can taste it with your tongue) which induces insects to visit the flower. Removing the stamens, you are left with the ovary. It is a slender green object with a more slender, hairy, upturned tip, at the end of which is the small knob-shaped stigma (Fig. 13a^6). If you are clever enough to cut the ovary longitudinally with a razor blade, you will be able to see the row of ovules inside; you will see them more easily with a hand lens (Fig. 13a^7).

An insect visiting the flower to suck the nectar (which it can reach easily owing to the stamen-sheath being open on the upper side) depresses the keel petals. As a result, the stigma protrudes, and then the hairy part below it, upon which the pollen has been deposited by the anthers. If the insect has visited another flower, it may bring pollen from that flower to the stigma of this one, and it will certainly carry some pollen away. In this kind of way, pollination is effected; and in some kinds of bean flowers there may be self-pollination within the keel. Pollen grains resting on the stigma form pollen tubes just as do the pollen grains of Vanda; the tubes grow down into the ovary and there the sexual process takes place.

As a result of pollination, the ovary begins to grow into a fruit, just as the ovary of an orchid does. The fruit in this case is a rather small flat bean-pod containing a few seeds. If you

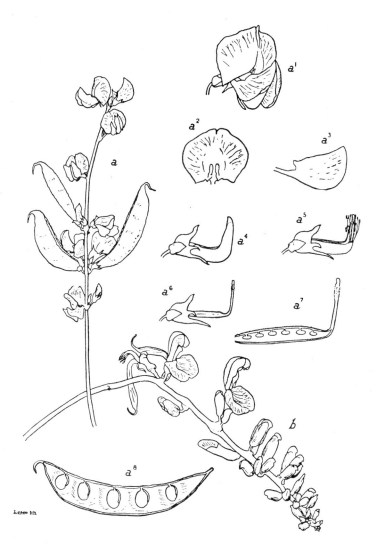

FIG. 13—(a) *Kachang Kara:* inflorescence × ½; (a^1) flower × 1; (a^2) standard
petal × 1; (a^3) wing petal × 1; (a^4) calyx and keel petals × 1; (a^5) stamen-keel
and free stamen above it × 1; (a^6) ovary, style and stigma × 1; (a^7) section of
ovary × 2½; (a^8) section of fruit × ¾; (b) inflorescence of sword bean × ½.

open a young fruit, you will see the developing seeds inside (Fig. 13a^8). They are all attached along one line, and the interior of the fruit is a single cavity. In many other kinds of fruits, there is more than one seed-containing cavity; and in some others (as in the orchid) the seeds are borne along more than one line in the sides of a single cavity. The bean-pod is, in fact, a very simple type of fruit. When it is ripe, it splits open along its two edges, and the seeds are liberated. Each seed is attached by a little stalk to the inside of the pod. The food material which the seed used in its growth all travelled along that little stalk. When the seed falls, the scar where the stalk was attached can be seen. In a Kachang Kara seed this scar is long and black.

Now look at the flower of a Sword bean or Kachang Parang. This flower has the same parts, arranged in almost the same way, as the flower of Kachang Kara, though somewhat larger, and the flower may be pink (there are pink and white kinds of Kachang Parang). But you will at once notice one difference, in the way the flower holds itself. The standard petal of a Kachang Parang flower is always more or less horizontal (whatever the direction of the inflorescence), and it acts as a landing-place for the large bees which visit these flowers (Fig. 13b). In this case the back of the bee comes into contact with the pollen, which it carries from flower to flower. The fruit of the Sword bean is much larger than that of the Kachang Kara, and has much larger seeds in it. If you look at a newly opened pod, you will see that the seeds are attached in one row, by little stalks, as in the other kind of bean; and the place where the stalk was attached to the bean is shown by a black scar.

If you soak a Sword bean in water for a few hours, remove it from the water and dry its surface, and then squeeze it gently, you will see that a drop of water comes from a little hole at one end of the stalk-scar. This little hole is called the micropyle (which is Greek for a small entrance). You will remember that the seed grew from an ovule. The ovule is covered with a protective coat, but at one end there is an opening in the coat, and through this opening the pollen tube can enter, carrying with it the male generative cell. When the ovule has grown into a seed, the protective coat becomes the skin of the seed, and in it is still the little opening or micropyle.

Now remove the skin from your soaked seed. Inside is the embryo, which consists mainly of two cotyledons. When considering the germination of the Rubber seed, we noted that the embryo in that seed has two cotyledons, but they are thin, and lie surrounded by a food-store called the *endosperm*. In the Sword bean there is no endosperm; all the food-store has been absorbed by the cotyledons during the development of the seed. This makes the process of germination a little simpler. The other parts of the embryo, namely the first root and the stembud, are also present; the first leaves on the stem-bud can be easily seen in this seed.

A third example of the bean family is the Dadap tree (*Erythrina indica*), which makes such a brilliant display of scarlet flowers in the early part of the year in the north of Malaya. A Dadap flower has exactly the same parts as a Sword bean flower, but it is larger and the parts are differently proportioned. The standard is again much the largest petal, and it is horizontal. The wings and keel petals (which are not joined together) are all about equal, but they are far too small to enclose the stamens, which stand erect, with the ovary, their tips curving over towards the standard. These flowers contain a great deal of nectar; it will spill out in quite large drops if you hold the flower in a suitable position. This nectar is taken by small birds (sunbirds and flower-peckers) which are attracted by the bright colour of the flowers. In sipping the nectar, these birds come into contact with the anthers, and so carry pollen from flower to flower, as the bees do for bean flowers. Dadap trees flower in dry weather, and it is suggested that in some places, where surface water is absent at such a season, the nectar of Dadap trees is an important source of water for the small birds concerned. After the Dadap flowers have withered, the ovaries of some of them grow into fruits. These are pods of the same general nature as bean-pods, but they are peculiar in being swollen only where the seeds develop, with constrictions between the seeds.

Now take a quite different type of flower, maize or jagong. Maize is really a kind of grass, with a stout stem and broad leaves. In due time it has a branched grass-like inflorescence (or tassel) at the top of the stem, and when this is ripe every puff of wind will bring a small cloud of pollen grains from it. The flowers in the tassel consist only of stamens, protected when young by little chaffy structures called glumes or bracts. There are no sepals or petals. Lower down the stem you will find one or more side-branches which are swollen and wrapped up with sheaths; out of the top of each such branch comes a bundle of delicate limp threads. These threads are the stigmas, and they come from very simple flowers, each of which consists of an ovary containing one ovule. If these ovules are to grow into seeds (i.e. if you are going to get a cob on your maize plant), each one of them must receive a pollen tube, and so each stigma must have at least one pollen grain placed on it. The placing of the pollen on the stigmas is done by the wind; or if you like you can do it by picking the tassel and shaking it above the tuft of stigmas. If you carefully protect the stigmas from the possibility of pollination, you will get no seeds.

A ripe cob of maize bears many seeds all over its surface. Each of these seeds is really a fruit, because it grew from an ovary containing one ovule; but the wall of the ovary is very thin, and unites with the coat of the seed, so that the fruit of maize functions as a seed.

There are many kinds of maize, the grains of which differ in colour and shape; some are white, some yellow, some red, and some nearly black. Some have a rather high sugar content, and these are wrinkled when dry. Some cobs of maize have all the seeds almost alike, but in some cobs there are obvious differences among the seeds. How does it happen that one plant can produce different kinds of seeds? Are not seeds intended to reproduce the plant? If they are not all alike, some of them will obviously produce plants unlike the parent which bore them.

The reason why some seeds may be unlike others, in the same cob, is that each seed is the result of a sexual process; its nature is determined partly by the male reproductive cell brought by the pollen tube, and partly by the female reproductive cell in the ovule. The reproductive cells are called *gametes*. When the gametes are formed, a peculiar process takes place. The details of this process are very complex and can only be seen after special preparation, and with the highest powers of the microscope. In the past half-century a great deal of time has been spent by many people, in many countries, in the study of this subject. Here we can only attempt a much simplified statement about it. Those who wish to read more should consult one of the recent popular works on genetics.

When we were considering the growth in thickness of the trunk of a tree, we discussed the activity of the cambium. Each cambium cell keeps on forming new cells by a process of division. The cambium cell divides, thus forming two cells. One of these will then form a cell of the wood, the other will first grow and then divide again. Growth always involves multiplication of cells by a process of the division of individual cells. Each cell has a *nucleus*, which is a special part of its protoplasm, enclosed by a fine membrane. Before a cell can divide and form two cells, the nucleus must divide, so that each new cell may have a nucleus. When division is to take place, the substance of the nucleus is concentrated into small bodies called *chromosomes*. The chromosomes are not all alike; each has its peculiar size and shape; and it has been proved that the chromosomes each include particular substances which determine particular characters of the plant. At every cell division, the same set of chromosomes appears, and each chromosome divides into two equal halves, one half going to each daughter nucleus.

When a cell in a stamen divides, in the process of forming pollen grains, something different happens. Instead of the chromosomes each dividing into two halves, they first meet in pairs (there are always an even number) and then the members of each pair separate, one going to each nucleus that is to form a pollen grain. Thus the nucleus of the pollen grain, and later of the male gamete it will produce in the pollen tube, has half the number of chromosomes which are found in the cells of the body of the plant which bore it. The same thing happens in the formation of the female gametes in the ovules. When a male and a female gamete meet, their nuclei unite, and so the united nucleus has the full double number of chromosomes, and the nuclei in the cells of the embryo which it forms will also have this double number.

Each nucleus in the body of a plant, therefore, has two sets of chromosomes, a maternal set and a paternal set. When reduction to the half number occurs, at the formation of pollen grains, each member of the maternal set pairs with the corresponding member of the paternal set. At this pairing, there may be some interchange of parts between the two chromosomes. If there are any differences between the members of the pair, the differences may be redistributed during the pairing, and the two chromosomes that separate to form the gametes may not be exactly like any in the body-cells of the plant.

"If there are any differences between the members of the pair." How should there be such differences? This can occur if pollen from one variety of maize alights on a stigma of another variety. The united nucleus will include maternal and paternal sets of chromosomes which are not exactly alike. The embryo so formed, and the plant into which it grows, will partake of the characters of both parents. It is called a *hybrid*.

When such a hybrid plant, in which the maternal and paternal chromosomes are not alike, forms its gametes, there will be rearrangements of the maternal and paternal characters, as above explained. When particular male and female gametes (of the same plant) so formed unite, there is the possibility that the united nucleus may be unlike the nuclei of the parent plant, and the seed so formed will grow into a plant unlike its parent. The offspring of hybrids, if their two sets of chromosomes have several differences, is always mixed; we say that they do not "breed true".

Now let us return to our Vanda Miss Joaquim. This is a hybrid, having been produced by crossing two distinct species of Vanda, namely *Vanda teres* from Burma and *Vanda Hookeriana* from Malaya. These two species differ in many characters of shape, size, and colour of the parts of their flowers. If then we self-pollinate Vanda Miss Joaquim, or if we pollinate it with pollen from one of the parents or from another true-breeding species, the offspring so formed will be mixed. It so happens that many seedlings of Vanda Miss Joaquim have been raised, and no two of them are alike. The differences in some cases are not great, but by careful comparison they can be detected. In this particular case, Vanda Miss Joaquim has been crossed with its parent species, and also with other true-breeding species of Vanda, with the special object of producing varied offspring, in order that good recombinations of the ultimate parental charac-

ters may be produced. If one of the many seedlings produces
flowers of peculiarly fine size, colour, and shape, that seedling
can be propagated by cuttings, as explained in Chapter 3.

Among the many seedlings raised from Vanda Miss Joaquim,
and from their offspring again, a number of such fine new
varieties have been selected, with varied combinations of the
good characters: vigour of growth, freedom of flowering, a good
size, good shape, and fine colour of flowers. The great variety
of garden flowers of all kinds (not only orchids) are produced
by a similar process of hybridization.

We can now come back to the second question set at the beginning of this chapter. Why should the plant produce seeds by an
elaborate process, instead of merely producing small tubers by
budding, as many yams do? The answer is that at every reduction division of nuclei which precedes the formation of gametes,
there is just a chance that something abnormal may occur, and
a gamete may be produced that is not quite like those of its
parent. As we have seen, once such a different gamete is formed,
we have a further possibility of the production of varied offspring
at the next generation. The sexual process thus provides the
possibility of varied offspring. On the other hand, a tuber produced from a bud is merely part of the original plant, formed by
a series of normal nuclear divisions, and so does not give the
same chance of variation.

If there were no chance of variation among the offspring of a
plant, there would be no possibility of evolution. It is because
variations have occurred, due to changes at the reduction division, that material has been provided for the process of natural
selection, which is part of the mechanism of evolution. And so
it has happened that through the ages plant life on the earth
has gradually changed, and it is still changing.

Man has discovered how to produce more abundant variation
than nature does, by artificial crossing of different species and
selection from the variation so caused; and by further breeding,
man can produce a much more rapid change than nature could
do. So it has happened in the past century, and more especially
in the past fifty years, that cultivated plants of all kinds have
enormously increased in variety and in excellence.

The case of rubber in Malaya is of interest in this connection.

The original Rubber trees were all grown from different seeds, and they were not exactly alike. When seeds from these trees were grown, and seeds of later generations, it was found that there was much variation in many characters, as already noted in Chapter 5. This variation is due to cross-pollination. The small flowers of Rubber trees are visited by small local insects (midges and small bees) which sometimes carry pollen from one tree to another, and perhaps pollen is also carried by wind. One way and another, natural cross-pollination has been sufficiently extensive to cause a large number of re-combinations of the heritable characters of the original trees.

The product of the rubber tree is latex. Trees which produce most latex have therefore been selected, and have been vegetatively propagated by budding. All the trees so propagated from one mother tree are called a *clone*. Attempts have been made to produce high-yielding seedlings by pollinating the flowers of one high-yielding clone with those of another high-yielding clone. The flowers of Rubber trees are very small, borne many together in one inflorescence. As in maize, there are separate male and female flowers; in each inflorescence there are few female flowers and many male ones. Artificial pollination is difficult because of inaccessibility of the flowers, and because the flowers are very small. It is necessary to protect the female flowers from all unwanted pollen, and this protection must begin before the flowers open. When they open, pollen from the chosen clone must be placed on the stigmas, and the flowers again protected while the fruit begins to form. A considerable number of cross-pollinations have been made in this way. The resulting seeds again show some variability when planted, both in yield of rubber and in other characters, but on the average they have a higher yield than unselected seedlings, and some may give even higher yields than either parent clone. A plantation of one of the best modern clones will give a yield four or five times greater than that of a plantation of mixed seedlings in the early years of the present century.

The next step should be to try to get new Rubber trees, perhaps of different natural species of Hevea. By crossing trees already in Malaya with such new trees, the range of possible variation would be increased, with again the possibility of valuable new characters occurring, such as vigour, disease-resistance, as well as high yield. This process has actually begun, but the difficulty is to get suitable new seeds from the home of the Para Rubber tree and of its near relatives.

In the case of Coconut palms, there is variation from tree to tree in yield of nuts, and also in various other characters such as colour and size of the nuts. It has been found that by taking seed nuts from trees giving a good yield, the average yield of a new plantation can be increased, but (so far as I know) there has not yet been any artificial cross-pollination of Coconut palms. As noted in Chapter 2, Coconut palms cannot be propagated vegetatively. Therefore we must always expect some variation among them.

Oil palms are the next most important oil crop in Malaya. They came from West Africa, and also show variation in many characters, including the amount of oil which a single fruit will yield. The oil here is found in the outer flesh of the fruit, not in the seed. Selection for fruits with a thick flesh has, therefore, been undertaken. Inside the flesh is a nut which has a very hard shell, and an oily kernel in it. Palms vary in the thickness of the shell. Nuts with a thin shell are obviously best, as it is easier to crack them, and also the proportion of outer flesh and kernel to total weight of fruit is increased when the shell is thin. Cross-pollination of Oil palms, with the object of combining these good characters and others, has been undertaken. But again, as vegetative propagation is impossible, uniformity is not obtained. It is necessary to self-pollinate the best seedlings, and then to do the same with their offspring, to attain greater uniformity. If self-pollination of individuals which conform to a selected type is carried out over several generations, the amount of variability is reduced. The number of generations necessary to eliminate variability depends on the amount of variation in the original parents. In Oil palms (which flower at six years old), this elimination is a slow business. But in cereals like maize and wheat (which must also be grown from seeds) selection is more rapid, and true-breeding races have been obtained by selection following cross-pollination.

G

CHAPTER SEVEN

FRUITS AND SEEDS

IN Chapter 1 we noted that in Singapore the Tĕmbusu trees all flower heavily about May. Their fruits are slow to develop, though they are small, and take about three months to ripen. At the fruiting season the trees are covered with large quantities of bright orange berries. When these are ripe, there is a nightly invasion of the large fruit bats called Kĕluang or flying-fox. These bats live in colonies, roosting in trees by day and flying at dusk to look for food. They do not normally roost anywhere in Singapore Island, and for months you may not see a single one of them. But they evidently have scouts, because as soon as the Tĕmbusu fruits are ripe the bats appear in very large numbers, and come every night until all the fruits are gone. Their noisy quarrelling is most unpleasant to hear in the darkness, and the ghostly flap of their wings, as they scatter from a tree when disturbed, has a most eerie sound. Before dawn the bats have left for their roosting place.

The Tĕmbusu fruits consist of a very astringent pulp with a number of very small hard seeds embedded in it. The Kĕluangs swallow the fruit and digest the pulp, but they cannot digest the seeds, and so the seeds pass through the digestive tract uninjured, and they are voided with the bats' excreta. In this way the Tĕmbusu seeds become scattered in large numbers over a considerable area of ground (the bats fly very fast and over long distances). Such dispersal is clearly of value to the Tĕmbusu, in ensuring that seeds will have suitable new places in which to grow. The seeds of Tĕmbusu can only germinate in open ground, not in deep shade of the forest. There are some patches of cleared land in Singapore in which large numbers of Tĕmbusu seedlings appear. So much so that if you want a Tĕmbusu tree for planting, the easiest thing is not to plant seeds (which are troublesome to handle and also slow in developing), but to go

82

to a convenient piece of waste ground and dig up some young trees already growing there.

Now consider a pineapple, which is certainly a very different fruit from a Těmbusu berry. They have, however, two things in common. They are both fleshy fruits, and both contain small hard, indigestible seeds. No doubt, therefore, the pineapple can have its seeds dispersed by animals which eat it. But the pineapple is not a native Malayan plant (it comes from tropical America) and its seedlings would probably not be able to maintain themselves in natural vegetation in Malaya, even if there were animals which regularly ate the fruits and so dispersed the seeds. However, there can be no doubt that both pineapple and Těmbusu are adapted for seed-dispersal by animals; the value of their fleshy fruits and small seeds to both plants is that these structures aid in seed dispersal.

The pineapple is obviously a complex fruit as compared with a Těmbusu berry, and the pineapple plant, being a monocotyledon, is very different in structure from a Těmbusu tree, having stems of limited growth in length and no increase in thickness. If you look at a flowering pineapple plant, you see that the small violet-coloured flowers are crowded into a dense head which is raised above the leaves on a stout stalk. The flowers are accompanied by small reddish leaves called bracts. If you cut through the head of flowers, you will see that there is a fleshy central axis, to which the flowers are attached. Above the flowers, the axis bears some more green leaves. The flowers have inferior ovaries (like an orchid) and these ovaries are all joined together and to the fleshy axis. When the flowers are faded, the fruit develops by a further enlargement of the fleshy axis and also of the ovaries. The ripe fruit consists of the whole inflorescence, not merely of the developed ovary of a single flower. If you cut a slice off the side of a ripe pineapple fruit, you cut through the ovaries of the flowers which were on that side of the inflorescence. You can see that each ovary consists of three parts, and each part may contain a small black seed. (Cultivated pineapples in Malaya normally have few seeds.)

There are several cultivated varieties of pineapple, and uniformity of these varieties is ensured by growing new plants from cuttings of old ones. The cuttings are made from side-branches below the fruit, or from the tuft of leaves produced above the fruit. It is possible to grow a new pineapple plant from a seed, but the seed is very small and cuttings grow more quickly. Also seeds may not produce plants exactly like their parents, and in practice they are only used as a means of producing new varieties. To obtain maximum variation among the seeds, it is necessary to cross-pollinate the flowers of one variety with pollen from another variety. The offspring of such a cross will include seedlings unlike either parent. New varieties of pineapple have been produced experimentally in this way in other countries, but little work of this kind has yet been done in Malaya.

Another curious fruit is the Jack-fruit (Nangka), which grows out from the trunk of a tree and is very large. The general structure of the fruit is not unlike that of a pineapple, but the seeds are large instead of small. Like the pineapple, the Jack-fruit develops from a whole inflorescence, not from a single flower. The fleshy part round each seed is formed from the calyx of a single flower; the ends of the calyces are joined together (Fig. 14a^2). The flowers are of very simple structure, and have no petals. Male and female flowers are in separate inflorescences. The male inflorescence is a club-shaped object (Fig. 14a), something similar to the fruit at a very early stage, and the small flowers quite cover its surface; each flower consists of a cup-shaped calyx and one stamen (Fig. 14a^1). When the pollen has been shed, the male inflorescence dies and falls.

There are several other trees in Malaya closely related to the Nangka (they belong to the genus Artocarpus), but all have smaller fruits. In most of them there is an edible flesh, and the seeds are also edible. Probably animals (monkeys, squirrels, etc.) taking these fruits eat both flesh and seeds; but they do not eat all the seeds, and so some are scattered to new places where they grow. One of the most striking of these Artocarpus trees, common in well-developed secondary forest in most of Malaya, is called Gĕtah Tĕrap. If you wound its bark, a very sticky latex exudes. Seedlings of this tree have very large, deeply lobed leaves; as the tree gets older, the later leaves are smaller and not lobed. The inflorescences are erect clubs on the small branches, not on the trunk.

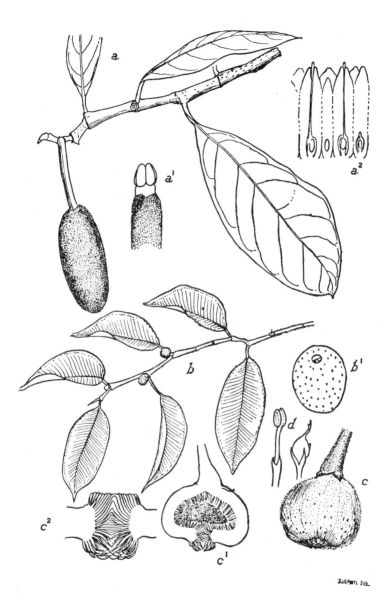

JURANI DE.

FIG. 14—(a) *Nangka:* branch with male inflorescence × ½; (a¹) single male flower × 10; (a²) section through outer part of young fruit, showing flowers fused together × 1½; (b) *Waringin:* twig with figs × ½; (b¹) a fig × 2; (c) *Ficus variegata:* fig × ½; (c¹) section of fig × ½; (c²) section of mouth of fig × 1½; (d) male and female flowers from a fig × 5.

Let us suppose that we can alter the shape of one of these club-shaped inflorescences. We first widen the base, so that the inflorescence is conical instead of club-shaped. Next suppose the cone is flattened into a disc, with the closely placed flowers all over its upper surface. Next imagine the middle of the disc depressed, so that we have a basin-shaped object. Finally contract the rim of the basin; we then have a hollow receptacle with the inner surface covered with small flowers. This is the structure of a fig, which belongs to the same family as Artocarpus, and there are actually other plants in the family (not Malayan) which have disc-shaped inflorescences.

There are a great many kinds of wild fig trees in Malaya, and some bushes and climbing plants which also bear figs. The fig genus is called Ficus. The size of the figs varies very much; few are as large as the edible fig of the Mediterranean region, and some are very small. If you cut a fig longitudinally, you see a cavity lined with very small round objects; these are the flowers (Fig. 14c^1). The fleshy part consists of the flask-shaped axis of the inflorescence. You also see a small opening at the end of the fig opposite to the stalk (Fig 14c^2). This opening has a number of small overlapping and interlocking scales, which almost close it. The fig flowers are pollinated by very small insects which can crawl past these scales into the cavity of the fig (or out of it).

In the Nangka fruit there are separate male and female inflorescences. The case of the fig is still more complicated, as there are three kinds of flowers. As in the Nangka, there are male flowers which have stamens, and female flowers each of which has an ovary and can produce a small fruit containing one seed. The third kind of flower is like a female flower but it cannot produce a seed. It serves to nourish the small insects which carry pollen from male to female flowers; it is called a *gall flower*. In some species of Ficus all three kinds of flowers are found in one fig. A wasp makes its way into the young fig and lays its eggs in the gall flowers. The eggs grow and finally hatch out as minute wasps in the cavity of the fig. The hatched wasps mate within the fig, and at the same time the male flowers shed their pollen. The female insects become covered with pollen, and carry some of it with them when they emerge from the fig. They then carry it to a young fig, and deposit it on the stigmas of the female flowers in that fig (thereby ensuring seed-production) while they lay their eggs in the gall flowers. And so the cycle is complete.

This kind of fig, containing all three kinds of flowers, is found on the Waringin tree (*Ficus benjamina*), which is often planted in Malaya, and on the sacred Indian Peepul and Banyan trees. All these trees have small figs (Fig. 14 *b*, *b*[1]). The figs are eaten by birds for the sake of their outer fleshy parts. The tiny fruits inside, each with a single seed in it, are hard and indigestible, and are scattered in the same way as Tembusu seeds in the birds' droppings. Thus the fig is not a fruit in the strict sense of being a developed ovary; it is a whole inflorescence, and the edible part consists of the hollow axis of the inflorescence.

There are other species of Ficus which have two kinds of figs, on different trees. The edible fig is one of these; a common Malayan example is *Ficus variegata* (Fig. 14*c*), which has many fruits on its trunk (see Chapter 1). The figs on one tree contain female flowers only. The figs on another tree contain male flowers and gall flowers. The wasps enter young figs of the second kind, and lay their eggs in the gall flowers. The eggs develop into larvae and finally the adult wasps emerge into the cavity of the fig and mate there. The male flowers around the entrance to the fig are then ripe and shed their pollen on the female insects as they leave the fig. These insects enter other figs if they can find them. Those that enter figs containing gall flowers repeat the egg-laying process; those that enter figs of the first kind find that the female flowers are unsuitable to receive their eggs, but they pollinate these flowers and die in the act of so doing.

The individual flowers inside a fig are very small (Fig. 14*d*). They can only be examined under a powerful lens after very careful preliminary dissection. They have a very small calyx and no petals. Male flowers have one or two stamens; female flowers have a small ovary containing one ovule. There is much more work to be done on the biology of Malayan figs. Any reader who may be interested to have further information about the details of flowers and figs of different kinds should consult Mr. Corner's papers in the *Journal of the Malayan Branch*,

Royal Asiatic Society (Vol. 11, pt. 1) and the *Gardens Bulletin* (Vol. 10, pt. 1).

A Guava is another fruit containing many small indigestible seeds like the Tembusu fruit, but larger. Its seeds are doubtless dispersed in the same way. But in the related Jambu fruits of different kinds, there is only one large seed in the pulp. This seed is usually not eaten, but dropped when the fruit has been consumed. The wild seashore Jambu (Jambu laut or *Eugenia grandis*), so much planted by roadsides in Singapore, has only a rather thin layer of flesh around its seed. Bats pick these fruits, carry them to their roosting places, nibble off the flesh, and drop the seeds. The bats often roost under the leaves of large fanpalms, and seedlings of Eugenia germinate abundantly near such roosting places.

The Mango family have a fleshy fruit with one seed in it, but the seed is covered by a sort of shell. This shell is formed from the inner part of the wall of the ovary, not from the seed; the seed is the kernel inside the shell. The shell is called the endocarp (inner part of the fruit). It protects the seed in some measure, but not from the sharp strong teeth of a monkey. Presumably the seeds of some wild mango fruits escape such attention. Sometimes the fruits merely fall to the ground and the seeds germinate there, under the old tree. Dispersal does not seem to be very efficient.

Some small seeds are dispersed by ants, not by birds or bats. These seeds must be small, or the ants could not carry them. They must also be of some use to the ants. It is found in fact that seeds dispersed by ants usually have a fatty substance in some part of them, which the ants eat. This does not involve the total destruction of the seed, which may germinate in the ants' nest and help to protect the nest. It is found that several of the plants that commonly grow in association with ants, and give shelter to them, have seeds which are carried about in this way. An example is the small-leaved Dischidia, which is a common creeping plant on old tree trunks (Fig. 15a). Though the Dischidia plant can live in very exposed places, the seedling needs some shelter, and this is provided by the ants.

A large proportion of fruits are not fleshy. Some are even hard and woody. Fruits which are not fleshy mostly open on the

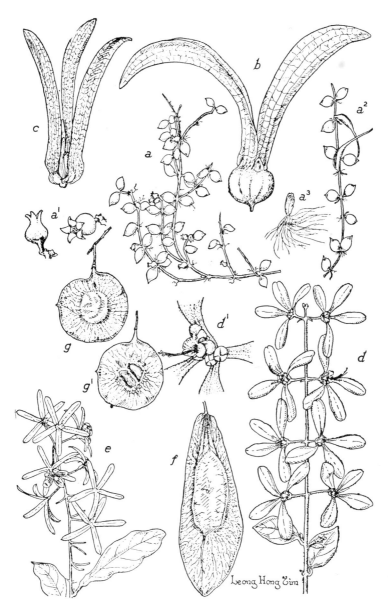

FIG. 15—(*a*) *Dischidia:* plant × ½; (*a*¹) with flowers enlarged; (*a*²) plant with two fruits × ½; (*a*³) seed enlarged; (*b*) *Dipterocarpus* fruit × ½; (*c*) *Shorea fruit* × ½; (*d*) *Congea* inflorescence × ½; (*d*¹) with flower enlarged; (*e*) *Petrea* inflorescence × ½; (*f*) fruit of *Koompassia* × ½; (*g*) fruits of *Pterocarpus*; (*g*¹) one cut to show seeds × ½.

tree and so liberate the seeds. Some, however, do not open, and these are mostly dispersed by wind or water. Fruits dispersed by wind include several which have a shuttlecock structure, spinning as they fall. The wings of the shuttlecock are formed from enlarged sepals in the fruits of many of our large forest trees in Malaya. These trees are called Dipterocarps (meaning two-wing fruits) because in some of them only two of the sepals form the wings (Fig. 15b). In the genus Shorea, which produces all the various grades of Měranti timber, three sepals are enlarged (Fig. 15c). But in the Chěngal and some other members of the family the wings are rot developed. The fruits fall straight to the ground, and as explained in Chapter 1, they germinate immediately. The spinning fruits of Shorea may travel some distance from the parent tree if they are blown clear of the crown of the tree above the rest of the forest, but once beneath the crowns of the trees they find little wind to move them. It is a matter for speculation whether the winged fruits of Shorea or the unwinged fruits of Chěngal are the more primitive.

Another plant with shuttlecocks, of a different nature, is the garden shrub called Congea (Fig. 15d). Congea is really a woody climber, and if it has a chance it will climb to the top of tall trees. In Kedah it may be found (with allied species also) climbing on trees on the edges of forests by roadsides. The flowers appear to have four unequal pink sepals. But if you look with a lens, you will find several separate flowers in the middle of the group of "sepals". Each flower has a cup-shaped hairy calyx, and the petals are also joined to form a small cup; the four stamens protrude from this cup. The four spreading sepal-like objects are small leaves belonging to the inflorescence; they are called bracts. If you pick a group of old flowers with their bracts, and throw the whole object into the air, it spins as it falls, in the same way as the Shorea fruits. So here the wings of the shuttlecock are bracts, not sepals, and in fact the object so dispersed is not a single flower, but a small group of flowers. Each flower should produce two small seeds, but in cultivation in Singapore these do not normally develop. I do not know why.

It is a strange thing that in the same family as Congea there is another genus, the flowers of which behave in a different way, though also spinning as they fall. This genus is Petrea, native in the West Indies, but commonly planted in Malayan gardens (Fig. 15*e*). Its flowers are borne in sprays six inches or so in length; each flower has a star-shaped lilac calyx and a cup-shaped deep violet corolla (petals and the cup to which they are joined). When the flower has faded, the corolla falls. Later the rest of the flower becomes detached, and at this stage it will spin as it falls, the lobes of the calyx acting as wings. So in these two genera of the same family with spinning fruits, one has wings made of sepals, the other of bracts.

Some dry one-seeded fruits are thin and flat, so that each fruit is like a single wing, and can be blown about by the wind. One big tree which has such fruits is the Kĕmpas (genus Koompassia), belonging to the bean family (Leguminosae). The fruits are like very thin pods with a flat seed in the middle (Fig. 15*f*). Another big tree of the same family with flat dry fruits is the Angsana, so much planted for avenues in Penang. The fruits are round, and usually contain two or three very small seeds in the slightly thickened central part (Fig. 15*g*).

If you inquire in a village market for a seed called Kĕmbang Sa-mangkok, you will get a smallish seed which swells when soaked in water and will ultimately form a cup full of gelatinous substance. This curious seed is actually produced on a winged fruit. The genus is called Scaphium, and it is related to Sterculia (see below). The fruit of Scaphium becomes quite large, with a thin wall forming a loose envelope around the seed. Ultimately the fruit splits open and becomes detached from the tree with the seed still adhering to it (Fig. 16*a*). The whole opened fruit thus becomes a wing or sail for the seed, and another name for this fruit is Sĕlayar.

However, in most cases where seeds are dispersed by wind, the fruit opens while still attached to the tree, and it is the seeds themselves which are winged or wing-like. The most remark-able of all such cases is *Oroxylum indicum*, a smallish tree with very large much-branched leaves which grows in secondary scrub or forest in many parts of Malaya. The inflorescences of this tree rise obliquely several feet into the air, bearing dull purplish rank-smelling flowers which are open at night and visited by bats, which drink their nectar. The flowers are fol-

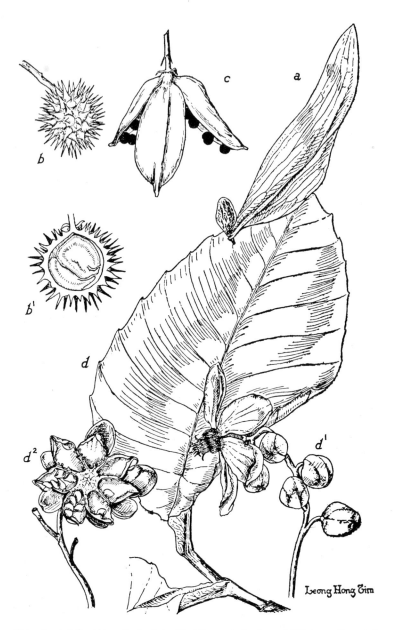

Leong Hong Tim

FIG. 16—(*a*) *Scaphium* fruit × ½; (*b*) *Allamanda* fruit, and (*b*¹) in section × ½; (*c*) *Sterculia* fruit × ½; (*d*) *Wormia:* leaf; (*d*¹) flower; (*d*²) open fruit × ½.

lowed by fruits which are sabre-shaped and may be a yard long
(Fig. 17a). They look something like gigantic flat bean-pods,
but inside they have a central partition with seeds on each side
of it. The seeds consist almost entirely of a wing (developed
from the seed-coat) which is as thin as tissue-paper but firmer
(Fig. 17a¹). The embryo is also very thin, and may be seen in the
middle of the seed. Embryo and wing together measure three
inches long and one and a half inches wide, or somewhat wider.
These extremely delicate winged seeds float gently on the air
in long gliding movements, carried along by the slightest puff of
wind.

The fruits and seeds of the African Tulip tree (Spathodea)
are very similar but on a much smaller scale; the fruits stand
erect instead of drooping, and they split down the middle of
each side instead of along the edges as in Oroxylum. Jacaranda
is another example of the same family with similar seeds but a
still shorter fruit.

Surprisingly, the other native Malayan plant with very large
thin wing-like seeds belongs to the gourd (cucumber) family.
This peculiar plant is a large climber in the forests of Pahang
and Selangor, known from few collections. Its fruits are as large
as a man's head and the outer part, instead of being fleshy,
becomes dry when ripe and breaks open irregularly to liberate
the seeds. This plant is called *Alsomitra macrocarpa*.

Another family in which winged seeds are common is the
Allamanda family (Apocynaceae). In Allamanda itself, the fruit
is about as big as a Rambutan and with rather similar but stiffer
prickles (Fig. 16b). The seeds are flat but the wing is not very
efficient for wind dispersal. But in the giant Jělutong trees
which belong to the same family, the seeds are paper-thin, and
an inch long. They are produced in horn-like paired fruits
which open in dry weather, setting free the seeds to be blown
away by the wind (Fig. 17, b¹–b³). The allied trees called Pulai
and Basong (genus Alstonia) have slender pendulous fruits, and
the seeds have a tuft of very delicate hairs which bear them up so
that they can float long distances in the wind, like thistledown.
The Oleander bushes of our gardens, imported from a drier
subtropical climate, sometimes produce fruits containing the
same kind of plumed seeds. The seeds of the curious plant

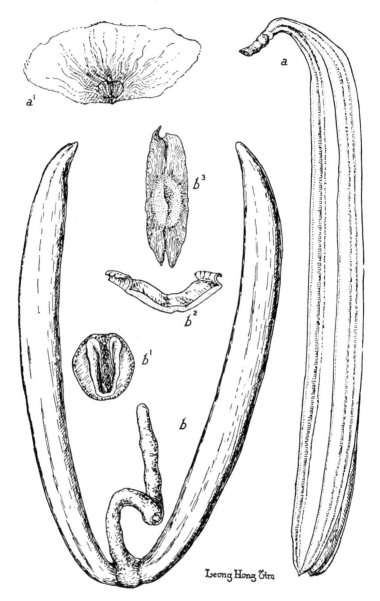

Leong Hong Vira

FIG. 17—(a) *Oroxylum:* fruit × ⅓; (*a¹*) seed × ½; (*b*) *Jĕlutong:* unripe fruit × ½; (*b¹*) section showing woody layer within × ½; (*b²*) part of opened fruit × ½; (*b³*) seed × ½.

called Dischidia (see Chapter 16) have also plumed seeds (Fig. 15a^3). The seeds of lalang grass are wind-borne owing to the presence of delicate hairs, but the hairs are not on the seed itself (see Chapter 9). Seeds of orchids are wind-borne because they are so very small (Chapter 10).

Next we may consider explosive fruits. Here the seeds themselves have no wings or other device to ensure dispersal, by wind or otherwise, but they are scattered by the explosive opening of the fruit. The most striking case is the Rubber tree. The hanging fruits are three-lobed. They have a green skin covering a firm inner part which finally becomes very hard and woody; the seeds are in three cavities in this woody fruit. The structure of the woody part of the fruit is such that, as it dries in ripening, internal tensions are set up within it. There are three places where there are layers of cells which are not woody. Breaking occurs along these layers when the internal tension reaches a certain strength. The fruit then opens explosively, with a sharp cracking noise, and the smooth seeds are scattered by force. This explosive opening occurs on hot days when the air is at its driest.

Explosive woody fruits are also borne by our forest climbers called Bauhinia. These climbers sometimes cover the crowns of big forest trees with orange flowers; they are mentioned in Chapter 13. They belong to the bean family, and their fruits are pods, but they are woody. As with the rubber fruit, the woody part is so constructed that tensions are set up when it dries, and when the pod splits open the two halves bend suddenly backwards, scattering the seeds. As they are produced at a great height, the scattering may be very effective. Because of the explosive nature of these fruits, and the great height at which they usually grow, it is very difficult to get seeds of these Bauhinias. The tree Bauhinias which grow further north than Malaya mostly have rather ordinary bean-like pods which sway in the wind and scatter the seeds without any explosion.

The common Balsam of our gardens (an "annual" plant) shows another example of an explosive fruit, on a much smaller scale. The fruit is green and not woody, but the internal stresses set up during ripening are very great, and the ripe fruit explodes violently at a touch, scattering the many small seeds.

There are some fruits which break open on the tree, and then depend on birds to distribute the seeds. One of the most striking is the Simpoh tree (Wormia) which is so common in open places in many parts of Malaya (Fig. 16d^2). The fruit consists of several small pod-like structures joined together along their inner edges. When they all open, the appearance is that of a star, each open pod forming one of the rays. Along each edge of each pod are small black seeds, each almost covered with bright red pulp. This pulp is a growth that develops around the seed, from its base, during ripening of the fruit; it is called an aril. Birds see the bright red aril, which they like to eat, and in so doing disperse the seeds. The fruits open before dawn, and you have to get up early if you want to find some seeds. The flesh on a Durian seed is also an aril, but the Durian fruit does not open on the tree to display it. Another aril is the mace of a nutmeg; there are many wild nutmegs in Malayan forests, all with brightly coloured mace which is displayed when the fruit opens.

Among the most brilliant of all Malayan fruits are those of several species of Sterculia. They are the most vivid red you can imagine, and fairly large. They open in the same way as Wormia fruits, but there are fewer parts and each is larger; and the seeds hang down (Fig. 16c). The black glistening seeds have no aril, but there is a thin pulpy layer beneath the black coat. Whether this is their only contribution of food to the birds that eat them is unknown.

Finally we come to water-borne fruits and seeds. Trees and other plants which live near the sea or near rivers often have fruits which can float and so are dispersed by sea currents or rivers. The most remarkable of all is the coconut, which when ripe has a very thick fibrous husk containing air-spaces. The fruit is thus able to float, and it can live for a long time floating in the sea. If cast up on a shore far enough from the sea, it can germinate.

If you walk along the seashore soon after a very high tide, you will find a number of different fruits and seeds which have been washed up by the sea and left stranded. Among them will be seeds of the Nipah palm and seashore Pandan (Chapter 2). Also you may find fruits of Cerbera (Malay Pongpong) nearly as big as tennis balls but ovoid; the small trees which bear them are common on muddy river banks near the sea and have pretty white flowers. Then there may be Heritiera fruits, shaped rather like the hull of a broad-beamed boat, with a small keel.

Besides the fruits, there may be floating seeds. You will find some that have one surface smooth and rounded, the others more or less flat and separated by sharp angles. These are Carapa seeds (Fig. 18a^1). Carapa trees (the Malay name is Nyireh) live in the mangrove and bear large spherical fruits. When a fruit breaks open, the seeds are liberated. They are closely packed in the spherical fruit, so that the sides in contact are flat and irregular in shape, meeting at sharp angles, whereas the side in contact with the outer wall of the fruit is rounded. The seeds have corky coats which give them buoyancy.

Also on the seashore you may find large numbers of seeds which have begun to germinate and have lost their seed-coats; you can see two green cotyledons and a well-developed root with side-roots. These seeds were borne by the mangrove trees called Api-api or Avicennia (Fig. 18d). They grow on the seaward fringe of the mangrove. When the fruits are ripe, the seeds germinate inside the fruit, absorbing food from the tree by a special arrangement not found in other plants. Eventually they burst the fruit and fall; they can float on the sea-water and can live for some time while floating. They can germinate and grow in places where they are covered by almost every tide, whereas most of the mangrove plants cannot.

The most remarkable of the mangrove fruits are those of the trees called Bakau, or Rhizophora. The fruits of these trees are not large. Each contains a single seed, which begins to grow while inside the fruit. The root of the seedling pierces the wall of the fruit and hangs downwards, while the cotyledons remain inside the fruit and are joined together with a solid tip that can absorb food from the tree. Eventually the seedling root may reach a length of eighteen inches or more, with a thickness of nearly an inch near the tip (Fig. 18b). When fully grown, the seedling drops off by separating itself from the cotyledon-tube, the scar of which forms a ring round the top of the fallen seedling; the small leaf-bud rises above this scar.

If the tide is low when the seedling falls, its tip will enter the mud (owing to the impetus of the fall), and so the seedling is

H

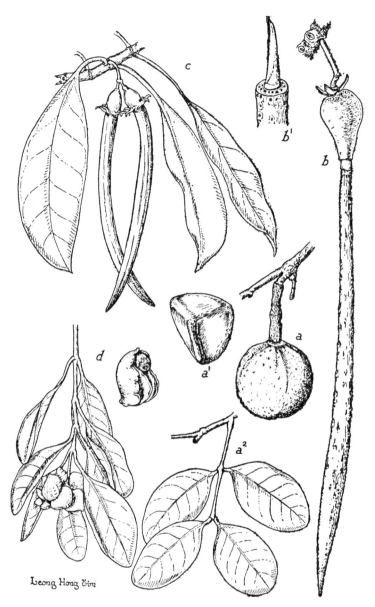

FIG. 18—(*a*) *Carapa:* young fruit; (*a*¹) seed; (*a*²) leaf × ½; (*b*) *Rhizophora:* seedling
hanging from tree × ⅓; (*b*¹) top of released seedling × 1; (*c*) *Bruguiera* branch
bearing seedlings × ½; (*d*) *Avicennia:* fruiting branch and germinating seed
× ½.

self-planted. If the tide is high, the seedling falls into the water, where it floats and is carried away by tidal currents.

Rhizophora trees grow in deep mud. As soon as the seedlings are a foot or two high, they produce roots from the stem; the roots grow outwards and downwards in a curve, and so form props or flying buttresses. As the young tree grows taller, it produces more and more of these prop-roots, which ensure its stability in the soft mud.

There is another genus of mangrove trees called Bruguiera, closely related to Rhizophora but growing in the less frequently flooded parts of the mangrove where the mud is not so soft. There are several species of Bruguiera, and some of them produce the most important timbers of the mangrove forest; the Malay name of one is Tumu. The fruits develop in the same way as those of Rhizophora, but the seedling roots never grow so long, and when the seedling is ready to fall the break occurs at the stalk of the fruit, not at the attachment of the cotyledons (Fig. 18c). Bruguiera trees have no prop-roots, but the base of the trunk has solid buttresses, which are connected to ridge-shaped roots running for a little distance along the surface of the mud. There are also erect knee-shaped branches which arise into the air from roots which are below the mud. These erect roots serve as breathing organs. The mud contains little oxygen, but the roots must have oxygen in order to live (see Chapter 15).

CHAPTER EIGHT

BANANAS

B ANANA plants are so peculiar in many ways, and so important in Malaya, that they merit a chapter to themselves, though in manner of growth they belong with the plants mentioned in Chapter 3.

A banana plant is propagated by suckers, which are side-shoots growing from the base of an old plant. A well-grown sucker appears to consist of a rather thick stem with a few leaves at the top. Actually what appears to be a stem consists of the bases of the leaves, which form tubular sheaths fitting closely one within the other. If you cut through such a sucker vertically, you will see that the true stem is very short; it is, in fact, about as tall as it is wide, and it continually produces new and larger leaves, each with a longer sheath than the last, until the full size of the plant is reached. Simultaneously the base of the stem bears a succession of roots, as the base of a palm trunk does.

A fully grown banana plant, before it flowers, thus consists of a "trunk" formed of concentric tubular leaf-sheaths, with the blades of the leaves spreading from the tops of the sheaths, and a short broad stem (hidden by the leaf-sheaths) at the base. Except for the shape of the leaf-blades, it is very like a young plant of a Royal palm which has not yet produced a true trunk. When the banana plant has produced all its leaves, the top of the stem forms the inflorescence, which proceeds to force its way up the centre of the "trunk".

At the time of flowering, the earlier (outer) leaves of a banana plant have shrivelled; their sheaths soon split owing to the increasing size of the later leaves which develop within them. But the sheaths of the later leaves, which do not split, must also be subject to much tension as others (and the flowering stem) grow within them, and they must be able to stretch somewhat without splitting.

The structure of the leaves is interesting. A cross-section through an old "trunk" shows the way the tubular sheaths fit inside each other. Each sheath is fairly thick, and there are many longitudinal air passages in it which show as holes in the section. Alternating with the air passages are vascular bundles, each of which has a bundle of fibres. A split leaf-sheath may be torn into shreds, each containing one or more vascular bundles. When the shreds are dried, they may be used as string, owing to the strength of the fibres in them. A slimy substance will ooze from cut sheaths. This substance (and all juices from cut parts of a banana plant), although colourless, will stain cotton cloth black, and such stains are very difficult to remove from clothing.

Though the leaf-sheath fibres of cultivated and wild bananas in Malaya are quite strong enough to be useful as string, they are much less strong than the fibres of a wild banana native in the Philippines. The fibres of this Philippine species (called *Musa textilis*, or Abaca) form Manila hemp, one of the world's most important commercial fibres.

The blade of a banana leaf has a stout midrib. The thin part of the blade has many closely parallel veins running almost at right angles to the midrib. There are no cross-veins, and it is easy to tear the blade between any two veins. Such tearing soon occurs in various places, as the leaf is blown about by the wind, and the blade of an old leaf may be torn to shreds which hang irregularly and limply from the midrib. But though torn, the leaf does not cease to function. Each shred has a vein (or veins) intact, and so it receives its normal water supply; and the food manufactured in its green cells can be carried away to the growing parts of the plant which need it. The tearing is in fact an adaptation, on the part of a broad leaf, to life in windy places.

A young leaf-blade, before it unfolds, is an erect, narrowly cylindrical object. If you examine it carefully, you will find the blade is folded in such a way that one half is rolled round the other, the inner half itself being also coiled. Owing to this unequal arrangement, the two halves of the fully grown leaf are seen to be somewhat unequal, at least at the base.

Now we come to the flowers. When the inflorescence appears, it is entirely enclosed by large overlapping (usually purplish) bracts; this mass of bracts is at the end of a stout green stem which usually bends over so that the tip of the inflorescence points horizontally or downwards, but in some wild bananas it is upright.

The large bracts of the inflorescence are arranged spirally (as are the leaves). Each bract in turn rolls backwards and exposes a group of flowers in its axil. The flowers have no individual bracts, though such bracts are present in allied families. The first few bracts enclose female flowers. The flowers under one bract are in two close rows, several in each row; each flower will ultimately produce a banana fruit, and the fruits are arranged in "hands", one hand being formed by the flowers in the axil of a single bract. After several groups of female flowers have appeared, the remaining bracts, which lie more closely together, contain male flowers only. The pendulous male tip of the inflorescence is called jantong in Malaya; the young flowers in it are edible.

The structure of the flowers is peculiar. In allied families, there are usually three sepals and three petals, all of them often joined to a basal tube or funnel. A banana flower has this structure except that one petal is quite free; the tube is thus split to the base on each side of this petal (Fig. 19, a^1–a^3). There are five stamens (six is normal in other families), the gap being opposite the free petal. (Compare with a ginger flower, in which there is only one stamen, and that opposite a petal, the other five being absent.) There is also a style and stigma, connected to an inferior ovary (compare with the Vanda flower described in Chapter 6). In the female flowers the stamens are present but have no pollen; in the male flowers, the female parts are all rudimentary.

Around the bases of the stamens a considerable amount of sweet nectar is produced. Owing to the presence of the free petal, this nectar is easily accessible. If you are near a flowering banana plant about eight or nine o'clock in the evening, you will notice the strong sour-sweet smell of the flowers, which is not unlike that of Durian flowers. The smell attracts bats to both banana and Durian flowers, and the bats lick the nectar from both. The rolled-back large bract of the banana inflorescence provides a convenient hold for a bat's claws; supported by its

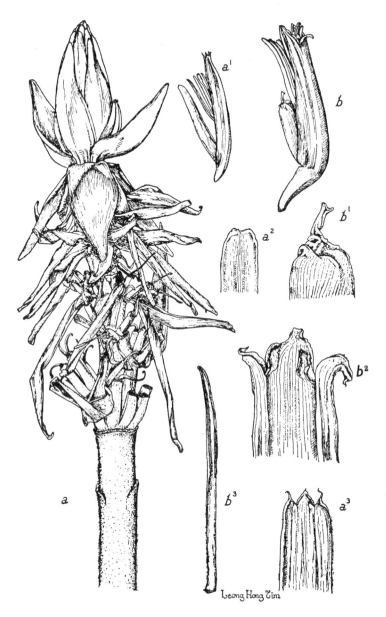

FIG. 19—(a) *Musa violascens:* inflorescence, with young fruits at base and male flowers at top × ½; (a¹) male flower × 1; (a²) tip of odd petal × 2; (a³) tips of united sepals and petals × 2; (b) edible banana: male flower × 1; (b¹) tip of odd petal × 2; (b²) tips of united sepals and petals × 2; (b³) stamen × 2.

claws (which are on the fore edge of the wings) the bat's head is in a position to insert its tongue into the flower and lick the nectar.

While taking the nectar, the bat also has pollen dusted on to its head, and this pollen may be passed to another flower. The pollen will, of course, be taken from a male flower, and can be transferred to the stigma of the female flower on another inflorescence. It so happens that pollination of female flowers of cultivated bananas is not necessary; the fruits have acquired the habit of developing without pollination, and anyway they have no seeds. But the wild bananas of Malaya do need pollination if they are to produce fruits, and their fruits are then filled with seeds; they contain very little edible pulp. No observation of bats on the wild banana inflorescences has been made, but it will probably be shown that bats visit and pollinate the flowers of those which have flowers newly open during the night.

The flowers of edible bananas and their wild allies agree with other flowers pollinated by bats (e.g. *Oroxylum indicum*, called "Midnight Horror" by Corner) in the following characters: dull colour (of bracts in the case of bananas), flowers open at night, strong rank scent, copious nectar.

As above mentioned, there are wild Malayan bananas of which the inflorescence is erect. The common species is called *Musa violascens* (Fig. 19a). In these cases, the bracts are a pretty bright lilac-mauve, or even partly white. It has been reported that the flowers of these bananas are bird-pollinated, not bat-pollinated. The bright colour attracts nectar-sucking birds, and the flowers are open in the day-time; the strong odour is unnecessary and is absent. But it should also be noted that male flowers of wild bananas of all kinds are visited by bees which collect pollen.

Bananas, both wild and edible, are all native of tropical Asia and Australasia. Their African allies are quite a distinct group of plants, and have produced no edible kinds. But bananas of Asian origin are now extensively cultivated both in Africa and the tropical parts of America and the West Indies, and the plantations of bananas in Jamaica and other parts of the West Indies provide the principal source of supply of these fruits for Europe. About the year 1920 it was discovered that a disease, called Panama disease, caused by a fungus that lived in soil, was a serious menace to the banana plantations of the West Indies. An infected plant could not be cured, and the fungus infection remained in the soil, so that other plants would be affected; sterilization of soil on the large scale was impossible. Other kinds of edible banana which were resistant to the disease had other characters which made them unsatisfactory for the export trade. It was therefore decided to undertake a programme of breeding, in the hope of producing a new banana combining disease-resistance with all the desirable qualities of the standard export variety which is called Gros Michel.

Gros Michel, like most edible bananas, will produce fruits with-out pollination of its flowers, and even if pollination occurs no seeds are normally produced; this is one of the important charac-ters of a good edible banana. But breeding is only possible through seed production, and it was therefore necessary to find seed-bear-ing bananas which might be used to hybridize with Gros Michel. Wild banana plants from Malaya and neighbouring countries were taken to Trinidad and Jamaica, and also the small edible Malayan banana Pisang Lilin, which often produces a few seeds. Experi-ment proved that the only way of obtaining promising new kinds of banana plant was by using these seed-bearing kinds as sources of pollen. In the first attempt to obtain seeds in this way 20,000 flowers of Gros Michel were pollinated, but only seventeen seeds resulted. The first generation hybrids were disease-resistant, but did not fully meet other requirements. To get a greater variety of seedlings, hybrids were then made between seed-bearing kinds, and pollen of these hybrids placed on the stigmas of flowers of Gros Michel. This breeding programme is still in progress; during its course a great deal of new information about bananas, both wild and cultivated, has developed.

CHAPTER NINE

GRASSES

GRASSES are an extraordinarily successful family of plants. They are not only one of the largest families in number of species, but also they cover large areas of ground, almost to the exclusion of members of other families, in many parts of the world. Grasses provide a great part of the food for grazing animals, and it is partly because of this that grassland persists in some countries; in the absence of grazing or mowing, such grassland would give place to scrub and ultimately to forest. The grass family also has provided the cereals rice, wheat, maize, oats, etc., which are the staple food of man.

Almost all grasses are sun-loving plants. They cannot exist in shady places. The natural vegetation of Malaya is a deeply shady forest, and in it is found only one kind of grass. In lightly shaded places, on the edges of forests and in small clearings, a few other grasses are found, but the great majority need full exposure to sun. Grasses therefore exist only where forest has been felled; they are mainly followers of man, and many of them have been brought by man (often accidentally) from other countries. The forest grass is called Leptaspis. It has very broad leaves, and peculiar flowers; it fruits are enclosed in small burs which adhere to passing animals.

Bamboos are usually included in the grass family, but they represent a very distinct group and are perhaps best ranked as a separate family of their own.

The grasses which occur in Malaya are so constituted that they can withstand a wet climate. It is a very striking fact that many species of grasses which have a wide natural distribution in drier countries, sometimes from Africa through India to Indo-China and also to Australia, do not occur in Malaya except in the extreme north (Kedah and Perlis, and to a less extent Kelantan) where there is a pronounced dry season. Some others occur in the north, and then on the sandy country near the east coast (where the sandy ground accentuates the effect of the dry weather which comes in the middle of the year) as far as Changi in Singapore, but not at all in the rest of Malaya. There are a few other such grasses which grow only on limestone, which again provides a quick-drying soil and so accentuates the effect of a short drought.

Grasses are monocotyledons. They have in many cases the habit of the bamboos described in Chapter 3; that is, each plant consists of a succession of erect branches of limited growth, each new branch arising from a bud at the base of an old one, and each bearing adventitious roots at the base. Unlike bamboos, however, grasses have terminal inflorescences on their erect shoots. But there are also many grasses which have a different habit. They produce creeping stems which go on growing horizontally for an indefinite distance, bearing roots at every node, bearing also axillary flowering branches which grow upwards from the node (Fig. 21b). It is this creeping habit which enables many grasses to cover large areas with a mat of interlacing leafy stems; it is the creeping habit also which enables grasses to survive and even flourish when mown closely and frequently, under conditions in which most other plants are killed. The creeping stems usually grow just on the surface of the ground, but in the case of lalang (discussed further below) these stems are underground.

In floras of other countries, grass plants are distinguished as annual and perennial. But the word annual has no meaning in Malaya, growth being possible from seeds at all times. We do have, however, some short-lived grass plants, which die after a few months' growth (perhaps in some cases only a few weeks) and are regenerated from seeds. Most Malayan grasses are of indefinite growth, and are potentially immortal, as are other creeping monocotyledons. The short-lived grasses all have a tufted habit.

Grass stems, like bamboo stems, are nearly always hollow, except at the nodes. The nodes are thickened, and they have a certain power of growth. If a grass stem is blown from an upright to a prostrate position, the tip of the stem can turn upwards owing to unequal growth of the two sides of one of the swollen nodes.

Grass flowers are produced on simple or branched inflorescences, but all have this in common, that the inflorescence
is almost fully developed inside a protecting leaf sheath. When
development has reached the right stage, the inflorescence
emerges from the shelter of the leaf (Fig. 20a); this emergence
is due to growth by the hidden base of the inflorescence-stalk,
which thus has to retain a youthful activity when the end of the
stalk bearing the flowering branches has ceased to have further
power of growth. This growth at the base of a stem when the
tip is no longer growing is called *intercalary* growth, and grasses
show one of the most remarkable examples of it.

In almost all other plants (including bamboos) every branch
of an inflorescence arises in the axil of a bract. But in grasses
such bracts are totally lacking. The cause of this is doubtless
that the leaf-sheath affords such excellent protection that there
is no longer any necessity for bracts at these places.

Grass flowers are very small. If you wish to examine their
structure, you need to have a lens mounted in such a way that
you can examine the flower through the lens and also have both
hands free to dissect the flower. Two needles are the best dis-
secting instruments, and a x10 lens will show essential details.

Though the flowers are very small, and simple in structure
individually, they are grouped together in a great variety of
ways, so that quite complex patterns of structure are formed, and
very careful observation is necessary to understand them. It is
not proposed here to deal with these structures in detail, but to
try to give some idea of their nature and significance.

Each grass flower consists normally of three or two stamens
(sometimes one, in a few cases six), an ovary with two stigmas,
and two minute objects called *lodicules*, which perhaps represent petals. This flower is enclosed by two very small bracts
which are usually green. But the unit of a grass inflorescence is
not a single flower; it is a *spikelet*, and each spikelet often contains more than one flower. In some grasses, of which the genus
Eragrostis provides some common examples, there are many
flowers in each spikelet, the outer bracts of the flowers forming
an overlapping two-ranked pattern (Fig. 20b). This is usually
regarded as the primitive form of spikelet, and other forms as
modifications of it. The most usual modification is a reduction

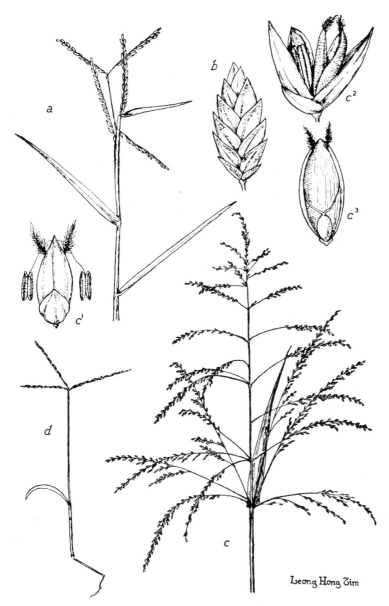

FIG. 20—(a) grass inflorescence emerging from sheath × ½; (b) spikelet of *Era-grostis* × 4; (c) Guinea grass: inflorescence × ¼; (c¹) spikelet × 6; (c²) opened spikelet × 6; (c³) palea enclosing ovary, with styles and protruding stigmas × 6; (d) *Digitaria* × ½.

of the spikelet to two flowers (one of them sometimes imperfect), or to one flower. At the base of every spikelet are two empty bracts, called *glumes*; these have a protective function, and have the same relation to the whole spikelet as sepals have to a flower-bud. Sometimes spikelets are in pairs, the members of the pair unequal.

The flowers and fruits (which are called grains) develop inside their small protective bracts. When the grain is ripe, it needs to be dispersed, or at least to fall to the ground, where the seed can grow. In the great majority of grasses, the grain is not liberated, but falls still protected by its bracts when it is ripe. In order that it may fall, or be carried away by some dispersal mechanism, the grain and its bracts must be freely detachable. There is, in fact, a specially constructed joint which makes this possible, and the exact position of the joint is one of the distinctive features of different kinds of grasses. But now note a remarkable fact. If the food-grains used by man fell to the ground in this way when they are ripe, the process of harvesting would be impossible. One of the things man has somehow done is to select for cultivation cereals which retain their ripe grains in the inflorescence.

Next we will consider briefly the way grass flowers work. If you go out in the morning and look at grass inflorescences, you will find that some of them have stamens hanging on very delicate filaments and swaying in the breeze. Others may have small spreading feathery stigmas. Both stamens and stigmas are often purplish, but some stamens are brown or yellowish and some stigmas are pure white. In the flower-bud these organs are folded inside their bracts until they are fully developed. Then one morning the two small lodicules become swollen and so separate the bracts that stamens and stigmas may emerge (Fig. 20c[1]). Sometimes there is only a small slit-like aperture on each side, sometimes the bracts gape widely. At the time of opening, the anthers of the stamens are fully developed, but the filaments are quite short. Within a few minutes, the very short filaments expand to twenty (or more) times their previous length, and are then very delicate threads, sensitive to every breath of wind. Soon after this, the pollen-sacs of the anther split open, and the pollen is soon carried away by the wind. Usually the stigmas emerge next day, or at some other time different from the stamens; in this way cross-pollination is ensured. The stigmas do not hang freely like the stamens, but usually project firmly one on each side of the spikelet; they have many spreading hairs throughout their length, and so are efficient in catching pollen grains. Each pair only need to collect one grain in order to produce a seed. When flowering is over the lodicules collapse and the two bracts fold together again to protect the developing fruit. At ripeness, the single seed inside the grain normally becomes quite fused with the thin wall of the ovary, so that fruit and seed are one. There are, however, a few grasses (including the common Sporobolus of Malaya) in which the seed is quite separate from the wall of the ovary.

The two bracts that protect a single grass flower have special names. The outer one (which you can see in many grasses without dissection) is called the *lemma*; the inner one (normally not seen) is called the *palea*. Each flower may be jointed separately, or the whole spikelet may be jointed at the base, above or below the glumes. There are also other possibilities, as we shall see.

There are some two hundred odd species of grasses in Malaya (excluding bamboos). They may be classified into two principal tribes and some smaller ones. One of the smaller tribes consists of rice and its wild relatives, and so is of great importance. We will deal briefly with the two great grass tribes, of which the basic genera are Panicum and Andropogon.

Guinea grass, a tall grass often grown as fodder, is called *Panicum maximum*, and is a convenient example of the Panicum tribe. It has a much-branched inflorescence (Fig. 20c), the branches very slender and bearing many spikelets which are about 3 mm. long. Each spikelet has one short glume and one much longer, and inside are two flowers (Fig. $20c^2$). The lower flower has only stamens; the upper flower has both stamens and ovary. Thus only the upper flower will produce a grain. The upper flower is also peculiar in another way. Its lemma and palea, which fit together very closely, are not green and leaf-like as are the glumes and the lemma of the lower flower; they are firm and pale, of a parchment-like appearance, and have curious transverse wrinkles. The firm lemma and palea form a very effective protection for the developing grain, and remain firmly enclosing the ripe grain. The whole apparatus is jointed at the base, and falls as one unit.

This arrangement of a firm lemma and palea enclosing flower and fruit is universal in the Panicum tribe. In some members of the tribe, the lower flower is represented by its lemma only; there are no stamens. Otherwise the spikelet structure is remarkably uniform throughout the tribe, though there are many different forms of branching of the inflorescence, which is in some cases a single unbranched spike, or a few such spikes. There seems no special mechanism of seed dispersal in most species of this tribe. The grain with its covering becomes detached and falls. There is no adaptation to wind dispersal, and no obvious adaptation to animal dispersal. Perhaps among many grains removed by animals a proportion are dropped and this suffices for dispersal. I have not seen a discussion of the matter.

Many Malayan grasses belong to this tribe. These include Serangoon grass (or *Digitaria didactyla*), which makes the finest lawns (Fig. 20d), and Carpet grass (*Axonopus affinis*), which makes a good strong turf and is also good for grazing (Fig. 21a). The only food-grain produced by the tribe is Setaria, or Italian Millet, which is sometimes grown between paddy crops when the land is dry. The distinctive feature of Setaria is that some slender branches of the inflorescence bear no spikelets. The whole inflorescence then consists of a close mass of slender bristles, among which are the spikelets, each producing its grain.

Two members of the Panicum tribe have remarkable and quite different adaptations to seashore life, and occur especially on the sandy east coast of Malaya. They are called Spinifex and Thuarea.

Spinifex has male and female flowers in separate inflorescences. The spikelets of female inflorescences are long and slender, and a large number are produced in such a way that they all radiate from one centre; the group of seed-bearing spikelets is thus a spherical mass of slender spine-like structures. When the grains are ripe, the whole mass of spikelets becomes detached as one unit, and it is well adapted to dispersal by wind on the open sandy ground close to the beach. Spinifex is abundant on the Trengganu coast, and extends southwards into Pahang, but does not reach the south of Malaya. The rhizomes of Spinifex

FIG. 21—(a) *Axonopus:* four inflorescences from one sheath × ½; (b) *Thuarea:*
creeping plant × ½; (b¹) inflorescence × 1; (b²) female flower × 4; (b³) old
inflorescence containing ripe grain × 1½; (c) *lalang:* part of inflorescence
bearing stalks of three pairs of spikelets × 3; (c¹) spikelet × 4; (d) Love grass:
group of three spikelets from front and back; (d¹) fruiting spikelet becoming
detached × 3.

I

are important in holding the loose sand, and so consolidating the ground near the sea, preparing it for other plants.

Thuarea is another sand-binding grass, but it is very different from Spinifex in habit and its dispersal adaptation, though like Spinifex it has separate male and female spikelets and an inflorescence that is detached as a whole for dispersal. The name Thuarea commemorates the French botanist Thouars, who described many plants from the islands of the Indian Ocean. The creeping stems of this plant are long and slender, bearing small leaves and short inflorescences (Fig. 21b). Each inflorescence consists of a single short spike with flattened axis, the few spikelets lying on one face of it. The basal spikelet contains one female flower; the rest have male flowers only. When the female flower has been pollinated and is developing its grain, the top of the flat inflorescence-axis curves over and forms a complete covering for the female spikelet. At ripeness, the whole spike becomes detached; it then consists of a small enclosed chamber containing a single grain. This hollow structure (containing air) floats easily and is dispersed by tidal currents.

The Andropogon tribe is characteristic especially of the drier parts of the tropics and subtropics, and most of the grasses which (as above noted) only occur in the north of Malaya belong to it. The tribe, however, includes also several well-known and very interesting grasses, and it also shows a very remarkable series of evolutionary changes in the inflorescence.

Everyone in Malaya knows lalang, which appears unasked in cleared and abandoned ground, especially in grassy places which are not regularly mown quite short. Everyone equally knows Sugar-cane (Tĕbu), though not everyone may have noticed its plumed inflorescences. At first sight, lalang and Sugar-cane might seem to be two very different grasses. But actually they are closely related, and both belong to the Andropogon tribe. In India, hybrids between lalang and Sugar-cane have been made experimentally. The habit of the two is certainly very different, but the inflorescences have a very similar structure, and they have what appears to be the basic structure in this tribe, for which reason we begin with them.

In both Panicum and Andropogon tribes, each spikelet consists normally of two flowers, though in many cases one of the flowers is imperfectly developed; in both tribes also the upper flower normally produces a grain, and not the lower. But in the Andropogon tribe the lemma and palea are thin and delicate structures, and the glumes provide the main protection for the flowers and developing grains. Though the lemmas may be delicate, they often terminate in a rather long, slender twisted bristle, called an *awn*. These bristles are the *pogon* or beard in the name Andropogon. The awns help to disperse the grains, as they twist and untwist in response to changes of humidity of the air. They may also help to bury the grains in the ground.

An inflorescence of lalang or Sugar-cane consists of many branches each with smaller branches, the spikelets being borne in pairs on short slender stalks (Figs. 21c, 23a). Each spikelet is jointed at the base, and becomes detached when the grain is ripe. The white fluffy appearance of the lalang inflorescence is due to the presence of very delicate silky hairs on the glumes (Fig. 21c[1]). When a spikelet containing a grain is detached, the hairy glumes ensure that it will be borne on the wind; its weight is very small and its air-resistance large. Lalang is, in fact, very efficiently dispersed to new places where it will grow, and we are all daily witnesses of this efficiency.

Another characteristic of lalang is of great practical importance, namely its subterranean creeping stem, and the erect habit of all its leafy shoots. Owing to the position of the stem, it is not killed when the leaves of the plant are burnt (they can easily be ignited in dry weather). Other plants growing with the lalang, which have not a protected underground stem, are killed by the fire, which thus establishes the possession of the ground by lalang. By repeated burning, which is often difficult to prevent, lalang may be the sole covering of land for many years. However, owing to the erect habit of each leafy shoot, lalang can easily be killed by frequent cutting to ground level. Such cutting does not kill creeping grasses, which are thus encouraged at the expense of the lalang.

Now let us consider Love-grass (*Chrysopogon aciculatus*). This is well known, owing to its stiff, upright inflorescence-stalks which can spoil the appearance of a lawn, and also owing to its detachable spikelets which can stick to one's clothing and are troublesome to remove. A Love-grass inflorescence is much smaller than a Sugar-cane inflorescence, but its organization is in some ways more complex. At the end of each branch of the inflorescence is a group of three spikelets (Fig. 21*d*). Only one of the three has a female flower; the other two are male and soon fall. When the grain is ripe, the seed-bearing spikelet becomes detached with a small stalk, and attached to it also are the stalks of the fallen male spikelets. The main stalk bears minute stiff hairs which lie obliquely; it is these hairs which provide the clinging character of the spikelet. In this case, there is adaptation to dispersal by animals.

A less well-known genus of grasses, but one which includes several very common species, is Ischaemum. Here the inflorescence usually consists of two short branches (Fig. 22*a*²). Each branch is jointed at short regular intervals (Fig. 22*a*¹), and when the grains are ripe the axis of the inflorescence breaks at the joints. Careful inspection shows that at the base of every segment of the axis are attached two spikelets, one stalked and one unstalked. The stalked spikelet is jointed at the base and when ripe falls, leaving its stalk behind. The unstalked spikelet develops its grain, and then the axis of the inflorescence breaks at the joint. Each fragment of the axis then bears at its base a spikelet containing a grain and also the stalk of the second spikelet (Fig. 22*a*²). This is the normal dispersal unit in a large number of the Andropogonoid grasses.

A further modification occurs in the genus Rottboellia and its allies, one of which (Fig. 22*b*) is not uncommon in Malaya (it is called *Coelorhachis glandulosa*). Here the Ischaemum structure occurs, but the axis of the inflorescence is hollowed to accommodate the unstalked spikelet and the stalk of the other. The whole inflorescence is thus smoothly cylindrical, and it breaks up into neat short cylinders each bearing one grain (Fig. 22, *b*¹, *b*²). In Coelorhachis there is a special group of cells at the base of each small cylinder; these cells contain a fatty substance much liked by ants, which accordingly disperse the seeds of the grass. I am indebted to Professor L. van der Pijl for pointing this out to me.

In most Panicoid grasses each erect stem terminates in an inflorescence, and new inflorescences only arise on new branches

FIG. 22—(a) *Ischaemum:* inflorescence × ½; (a¹) inner view of jointed zig-zag axis of inflorescence × 6; (a²) single unit consisting of 2 spikelets; stalk of stalked spikelet is on the right × 6; (b) *Coelorachis:* part of plant with inflorescences × ½; (b¹) seed-bearing spikelet on right, reduced stalked spikelet on left × 6; (b²) back view of b¹, showing swollen joint of axis × 6.

which come from the base of the plant.   In the Andropogon tribe
it is common for erect stems to have not only a terminal inflorescence but also others on side-branches (also more or less

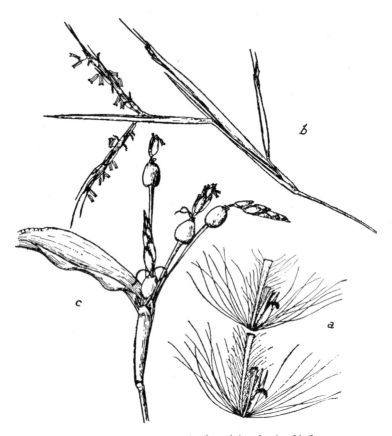

FIG. 23—(*a*) sugar-cane: two internodes from jointed axis of inflorescence; one
spikelet of each pair has fallen × 3; (*b*) citronella-grass: small part of inflorescence × 4; (*c*) Job's Tears: four branches of inflorescence × 1.

erect) which arise in the axils of leaves on this stem. This can be
seen on well-grown plants of Love-grass (where it is not in a
closely mown lawn). It is carried to an extreme development in
a few genera, notably Themeda and Citronella grass (*Cymbopogon
nardus* (Fig. 23*b*)). Themeda is a very tall grass which is

common on banks by roadsides almost everywhere in Malaya. It can be identified at once by the graceful pendulous branches of the much-branched inflorescence. Each branch ends in a spike consisting of only a few spikelets, and at the base of the little spike is a small leaf. This is quite a different kind of branched inflorescence from that of Lallang or Sugar-cane. Within the tribe can be seen a reduction from the Lallang type of inflorescence to the Ischaemum type with two short spikes, and then to the building up of the Themeda type in which there are many small Ischaemum-like inflorescences each on its own slender stalk, the whole complex branching system forming a new type of inflorescence. The final stage in this evolutionary series is reached by a grass called Apluda, in which each ultimate spike is reduced to three spikelets, only one of which has a female flower. In Malaya, Apluda is only found in the north and near the east coast.

In some parts of Malaya, Job's Tears (*Coix lachryma-jobi*) is grown on the drier land between rice crops. The inflorescence consists of many branches, somewhat in the manner of Themeda, each branch consisting of one basal spikelet containing a female flower, and several pairs of purely male spikelets (Fig. 23c). The basal female spikelet is surrounded by a curious flask-shaped bract, which becomes quite hard like a shell of a nut, and is usually bluish to nearly white. This bract encloses not only the female spikelet and its developing grain, but also the axis of the spike which bears the upper male spikelets. In some varieties of Job's Tears the shells are so hard that they are difficult to break. They are not much used except as beads, and the leafy part of the plant as fodder. But there are other kinds with thin shells, and these may give quite useful cereal crops, as the grains are fairly large.

Maize has the same kind of division between male and female parts of the inflorescence found in Job's Tears, but carried to an extreme degree. The top of a Maize plant bears a branched inflorescence not unlike that of Guinea grass, but it contains male flowers only. Female flowers are on short lateral branches, and they are quite enclosed by leaf-sheaths except for the long protruding stigmas. If the sheaths are removed from a young female inflorescence of Maize, the glumes and other small bracts may be found, showing that each grain of Maize is actually developed from a much-reduced spikelet of the same essential nature as the spikelets of other grasses. Occasionally freak plants are found with a few female flowers on the male part of the inflorescence.

CHAPTER TEN

THE STORY OF THE PIGEON ORCHID

THE Pigeon orchid grows on almost every old tree in open country in Malaya, though not in the deep shade of the forest. It is, in fact, so common a plant that everyone in Malaya who takes the trouble to read this book must surely have seen and marvelled at its graceful and fragrant white flowers which appear so suddenly and fade all too soon. The life history of this orchid is typical of many other Malayan orchids, and has many peculiar features.

In the first place, the Pigeon orchid is an *epiphyte*. That is, it grows upon another plant; it uses a tree as a support, and has become so far adapted to this kind of growing-place that it is incapable of growing on the ground. Many people think epiphytic orchids are parasites, but that is not true. A parasite takes its food direct from the living substance of its host. An orchid is quite external to the tree which bears it, and the only substance it absorbs from the tree is taken from the dead and decaying outer bark.

An epiphyte has its roots more or less exposed to the air. On a dry day, therefore, the roots are a liability to the plant, not an asset like the roots of a tree which permeate the soil and gather water from the soil continuously. An epiphyte can only absorb water during or soon after rain, or from dew at night. It must, therefore, be able to live from one rain to the next without losing too much water. Epiphytic orchids meet this requirement in two chief ways: they store water in stem and leaves, which are more or less succulent; and they prevent too rapid loss of water by covering their leaves with a waterproof cuticle. They also have a special root structure. The outer part of the root is a sponge which absorbs water rapidly, but when it is dry it also forms a buffer between the living interior of the root and the dry outer air.

The continuously wet and warm climate of Malaya makes the existence of epiphytes possible, and over some millions of years a very large number of epiphytes have come into existence by the process of evolution. They occupy growing room which other plants cannot use, and thereby escape having to compete with plants that root in the earth. Many of them occupy places where the light is brighter than the light on the floor of the forest, which is the alternative place for a small plant in the natural vegetation of Malaya.

Some epiphytes are adapted to life in exposed places, in the crowns of tall forest trees, or on trunks of trees in the open. Others can only live in deep shade and in a continuously moist atmosphere; such are found especially in the cloud zones of the mountains where vegetation may be dripping wet for several days at a stretch. There are all gradations between these extremes. The Pigeon orchid is one of the former extreme; it will only grow in rather exposed places.

In Chapter 6 we discussed the flower of Vanda Miss Joaquim. Almost all orchids agree with Vanda in the presence of three sepals, three petals (one being the lip), and a column with single stamen at the top. But the Pigeon orchid and its allies, belonging to the genus Dendrobium, show various differences from Vanda in the shape and interrelations of the parts. The first difference is that the column is very short (Fig. 24h), and has an outgrowth at right angles to its base (Fig. 24, f, g). This outgrowth, called the *column-foot*, is much longer than the column itself, and the bases of the lateral sepals are attached throughout the length of the column-foot. The lip is attached by its narrow base to the tip of the column-foot (Fig. 24f), and the bases of the lip and of the lateral sepals form a closed pouch which contains nectar (there is a nectary on the foot). It is this pouch (Latin, *crumen*) which gives the name *Dendrobium crumenatum*.

If you have Pigeon orchid plants near your house, you may wake up at dawn and smell their delightful fragrance (which is almost too powerful at close quarters). This fragrance and the white colour of the flowers attract bees, which come soon after dawn and visit the flowers to suck their nectar. In pushing its way down into the pouch of the flower, a bee's back comes into contact with the anther, and the bee may emerge with pollinia

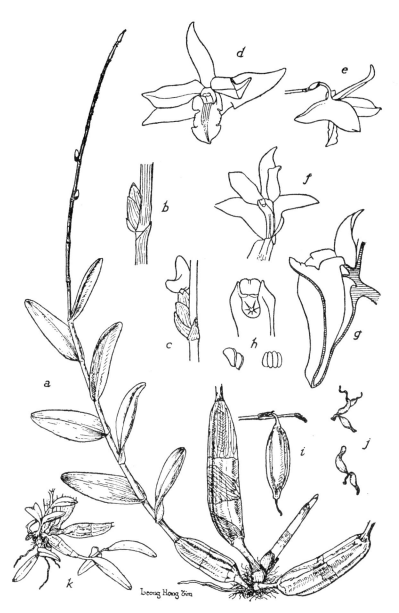

FIG. 24—*Dendrobium crumenatum:* (*a*) growing part of plant with a new shoot × ½; (*b*) inflorescence breaking through leaf-sheath × 2; (*c*) flower-bud × 2; (*d*) flower × 1; (*e*) side-view of flower, showing mentum × ¾; (*f*) flower with lip pulled down, showing column-foot × ¾; (*g*) vertical section of flower × 2; (*h*) column, and pollinia × 5; (*i*) fruit × ¾; (*j*) seeds, much enlarged; (*k*) young plant × ½.

attached behind its head. The pollinia here are four, in two pairs (Fig. 24*h*); there is no disc like that in Vanda, but there is a viscid substance just under the front of the anther, and this provides an adhesive. A bee carrying pollinia may deposit them into the hollow stigma of the next flower it visits. A large proportion of Pigeon orchid flowers are usually visited quite early in the morning. Soon after noon the flowers begin to close, and next morning they are quite closed. Those which will form fruits persist, and the floral parts gradually shrivel without falling; those that will not form fruits soon drop to the ground.

The fact that all Pigeon orchid plants flower simultaneously, although the flowers last such a short time, has interested many observers. The stimulus which leads to this simultaneous flowering has been discovered, but the mechanism by which the stimulus (or trigger) leads to the final result is unknown. The significance to the plant is clear. If flowers are very short-lived, there must be some way of ensuring that several are open simultaneously; otherwise the majority of flowers might be solitary and cross-pollination would be impossible. There is some evidence that self-pollination in this species does not usually lead to setting of fruit.

If you look at the slender terminal part of a Pigeon orchid stem, you will find that it is covered with sheaths, each attached at a slightly thickened ring on the stem. These sheaths are reduced leaves (they have no blades), and in the axil of each may develop a small inflorescence, which first causes a swelling and then a split in the base of the sheath (Fig. 24*b*). The inflorescence remains very short, and produces several flowers, one at a time, each protected when young by a small chaffy bract. A flower bud in such a position develops until all the essential parts are formed and the anther is almost fully grown. The bud then stops growing, and waits for the stimulus. The stimulus is an unusually cool day (a cool night is not enough), which in most cases means a sudden storm which cools the air some 10° F. It has been asserted that the sudden cooling is the essential stimulus; but it has also been proved experimentally that cooling which is gradual, if sufficiently long maintained (twenty-four hours), is sufficient. Probably both forms of stimulus are effective. In any case, it takes exactly nine days from receipt of stimulus to full development of the flower. The flower always opens just before dawn; this must be a response to another stimulus, perhaps rising temperature.

There are other flowers which respond to a temperature stimulus. We will revert to them later. In the meantime we will pursue the life story of the Pigeon orchid.

A pollinated flower forms a fruit. The fruit hangs down, and is an ellipsoid object less than an inch long (Fig. 24*i*). It ripens in about three months. As it ripens it turns slightly yellowish, but it does not become shrivelled, and the exact time of ripeness is not easy to judge. If you look at such a fruit every morning, one day you will see three little slits beginning to form near the pendulous tip. These slits soon elongate until they reach halfway up the fruit or further. Before that happens, the countless tiny pale greenish seeds (Fig. 24*j*) begin to fall through the slits as the fruit is shaken by slight puffs of wind. The seeds are so minute that they are carried away like dust.

If you look at a Pigeon orchid seed under a microscope that will magnify it about fifty times, you will see that it consists of a loose elliptic outer envelope, and inside this (faintly seen in outline) is a minute round embryo. The embryo has neither cotyledon, root, nor stem-bud, but it has a potential growing point. The embryo is so small that it contains very little reserve of food, and perhaps for this reason it has no power of germinating without help from another organism. The other organism is a fungus. The necessary fungus is evidently not uncommon on bark of trees, and in other such places. Threads of the fungus invade the base of the embryo, and enter the cells. At the same time, other parts of the threads are outside, in crevices of bark or other decaying material. It seems that the fungus threads can take up some food from the bark and pass it on to the developing embryo. Exactly what food is so transmitted has not been demonstrated, but it seems clear that carbohydrates (doubtless in the soluble form of sugars) are among the substances provided for the orchid by the fungus. It has been shown experimentally that without infection by the right fungus an orchid seed will not germinate, though it is provided with all the salts normally necessary for growth of plants. It has further been shown that without a fungus, but with sugar, the seeds will germinate, so the conclusion has been reached that the fungus supplies sugar, which it produces by breakdown of decaying bark and other material; but it may also supply other substances.

The germinating seed soon forms a minute green spherical mass, with tiny hairs on its lower surface, like root hairs. Next a very small leaf and a very small root appear on the spherical mass, and after that further leaves, a stem, and roots are formed in the usual way.

The structure of the young Pigeon orchid plant is like that of the orchids described in Chapter 3; that is, each stem is of limited growth, and new stems grow from buds at the base of old ones. Roots are formed by the basal part of each new stem. The structure of the individual stems is peculiar. If you look at a very young Pigeon orchid plant (they are the only common orchid seedlings on old trees in open places), you will see that each new stem is larger than the last, but all are short and fleshy, more or less cigar-shaped, and each bears one or two small fleshy leaves at the top, each leaf with a sheathing base (Fig. 24k). Sooner or later a stem develops an elongated slender terminal part, beyond the cigar-shaped base. This terminal part carries more leaves, the sheaths of which quite cover the stem. The swollen basal part of the stem is covered with sheaths only (i.e. leaves lacking blades), and roots are borne by the slender base of the stem, below the swollen part. The final development is that the apical part of a long stem bears sheaths only (blade-less leaves) and the flowers develop in the axils of these sheaths. Each new stem of a fully developed plant then consists of: (1) slender root-bearing basal part; (2) swollen part; (3) slender leafy part; (4) slender flower-bearing part (Fig. 24a). All parts are covered with sheaths, but the only leaves with blades are developed on part (3).

The stem bears no roots above the base. But an old plant often seems to bear a tangle of roots from the upper parts of its old stems. These roots are actually produced by new small plants which develop from lateral buds. Each new plant follows the same series of developmental changes as a seedling, but more rapidly, as it is nourished by the old stem which bears it.

Now we have followed through the life history of a Pigeon

orchid plant, we can see the way in which the different parts of the story are related, and how each structure is adapted to the peculiar way of life of the plant. The minute seed is adapted to wind dispersal, and the large number of seeds ensures that a proportion of them will find a suitable place to grow. The seed sacrifices size to mobility, and so has little food to start it in life, but it is adapted to receive help from the fungus. (As soon as the young orchid plant has green leaves it can make its own carbohydrates like other plants, but it retains a fungus infection; whether the fungus continues to play an important part in the life of the mature plant is not certain.) The fleshy stem and fleshy leaves contain water-storage cells. They enable the plant to live in exposed places on trees by tiding it over from one rain to the next. The leaves also have a thick cuticle which prevents rapid water-loss. The roots have a spongy outer layer and are adapted to absorb rain and dew; they are also adapted to withstand drying winds, and in fact will not live if they are deprived of a free circulation of air.

The sheaths on the upper part of the stem protect the growing flower buds. The buds grow to a certain size and then wait for a stimulus. The response to the stimulus of low temperature has two effects. Low temperature during the day almost always accompanies rain, and therefore the plant should have a new supply of water (which it can store); this water will be needed for the formation of the delicate flowers and to make good the evaporation from these flowers. The simultaneous starting of growth of all resting buds also means that all will flower together, and this ensures a greater degree of cross-pollination than would otherwise be possible.

The structure of the flower is such that a visiting bee inevitably carries away the pollen and is almost certain to carry it to another flower. The fact that all the pollen from one flower is carried away by one bee means that in visiting another flower the bee places many thousands of pollen grains simultaneously on the stigma, and this ensures the formation of many thousands of seeds. So the adaptation to insect visits and the formation of small seeds, the adaptation to wind dispersal, to fungus assistance and growth on the branch of a tree instead of on the ground, are all intricately interconnected.

There are a very great many orchids in Malaya (about eight hundred species are already known) and a considerable proportion of them are epiphytes. As indicated above, they live in a great variety of habitats, and they are adapted to epiphytic life by a great variety in detail of structure. Except for those which live under constantly moist conditions, they all have some method of storing water, in stem or leaves or both. The water-storing stem may be short and thick (often egg-shaped), or long and thinner; it may bear few or many leaves. The leaves may be thick or thin, and vary greatly in size and shape. All epiphytic orchids have a special arrangement for shedding their leaves. There is a joint at the place where the blade joins the sheath, so that in dry weather the blade can be shed and loss of water thereby reduced. In countries north of Malaya, where there is a regular and fairly long dry season every year, epiphytic orchids shed their leaves in the dry weather, like deciduous trees. In Malaya, this is unnecessary except in the north, and orchids usually retain their leaves throughout the year, though they may only make new growth (which needs extra water-supply) in the wetter part of the year.

As mentioned in Chapter 3, a bulb-shaped orchid stem which stores water (and some food) in the same way as a bulb does, is called a pseudobulb. This is a clumsy word, but it is well established in orchid literature. So any fleshy orchid stem, whether bulb-shaped or not, may be called a pseudobulb, or even a bulb. Some pseudobulbs have a single leaf at the top, some two leaves, or even more than two. One orchid genus is called Bulbophyllum and it includes a large number of Malayan species. The name Bulbophyllum was given because all members of the genus have pseudobulbs each bearing a single leaf (Fig. 25). The size and shape of the pseudobulbs varies greatly. There are, however, other Malayan orchids which have a closely similar vegetative habit, but they are not included in the genus Bulbophyllum because of differences in the flowers. Orchids, like other plants, are classified according to floral structures, because it is considered that such a classification best shows the true inter-relationships of plants.

As described in Chapter 3, the majority of orchids are sympodial in structure, each new stem being of limited growth. In some cases the new stem, starting from a bud at the base of an older stem, grows first horizontally, with only a short upturned leaf-bearing end. This is the case with most Bulbophyllums. The horizontal part of each new growth is called a rhizome. The rhizome is covered when young by sheaths (imperfect leaves)

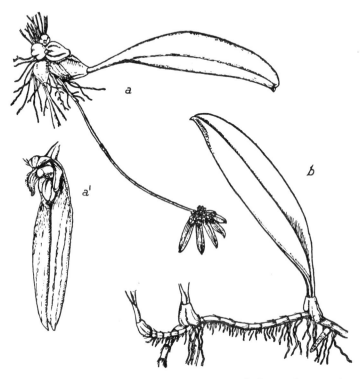

FIG. 25—(*a*) a small-flowered *Bulbophyllum* × ½; (*a¹*) flower of *a* × 2; lateral sepals are joined along one edge; (*b*) another *Bulbophyllum*, having a long rhizome between pseudo-bulbs × ½.

and bears roots; the upturned terminal part of each piece of rhizome in Bulbophyllum is a pseudobulb consisting of a single internode (i.e. no leaf is borne between base and apex of the pseudobulb). The next new stem of the Bulbophyllum plant is formed from a bud at the base of the last pseudobulb, and the inflorescences arise from buds in a similar position. An old plant appears to consist of a rhizome bearing a series of pseudo-

K

bulbs at intervals, but really each pseudobulb is terminal on its own section of rhizome.

Flowers of Bulbophyllum are in most cases very small, but a few are an inch or more in diameter. A well-developed column-foot is present, curved forwards from the base of the column, but the lateral sepals are not attached throughout its length, so that the flower has no pouch as in Dendrobium. The lip is attached to the end of the column-foot. It is small, fleshy, and tongue-shaped, and is very lightly hinged so that it moves very easily when touched or when the flower is disturbed. The column is short, constructed much as in Dendrobium. If an insect of an appropriate size lands on the lip of a Bulbophyllum flower, the weight of the insect upsets the equilibrium of the lip, which moves in such a way that the insect is brought into contact with the anther and removes the pollinia while freeing itself. A remarkable case is shown by *B. megalanthum*. Insects are attracted by the scent of the flower, and alight on the upper sepal, which is smooth. An insect in this position slips and falls on to the lip, which tips it, tail first, towards the column. The insect departs with pollinia on the hinder part of its body, and so can pollinate the next flower it visits. If too small an insect visits such a flower, it may be deposited tail first into the stigmatic hollow, and such insects are sometimes stuck fast in the stigma, so that they are unable to move. This seems to be a case of accidental misuse of a pollination mechanism. Some kinds of Bulbophyllum have long lateral sepals joined together, as shown in Fig. 25a[1].

Coelogyne has fewer species than Bulbophyllum, but the plants are mostly larger, in some cases much larger. A Coelogyne plant consists of a series of pseudobulbs, often with only a short length of rhizome between them. The pseudobulbs are fairly large, in some cases nearly as big as one's fist, and in others longer and rather slender. Each pseudobulb bears one or two leaves at the top (most species have two leaves). The leaves are thin and more or less pleated, but less so than in Spathoglottis. The inflorescence (if any) grows from the top of the pseudobulb. It carries a number of flowers, which in some species open one at a time and in others all together. The flowers have a long column without a foot, and curious wings around the anther.

The lip is large and has keels on it which are sometimes warty or crested. The flowers are in most cases scented and the scent attracts pollinating insects. An insect of suitable size, seeking nectar at the base of the lip, inevitably comes into contact with the anther on retreating, and removes the pollinia. The wings at the top of the column help to direct the front of the insect's body into the exact position required. There are two pairs of pollinia, each with an elastic stalk by which it is connected with the viscid mass of cells which becomes attached to the insect.

There is an interesting variety in growth-form within the genus Coelogyne. As noted above, in all cases the inflorescence (if any) grows from the apex of the pseudobulb. In some cases the pseudobulb and its leaves are fully formed before the inflorescence grows; in other cases the inflorescence develops simultaneously with the leaves and pseudobulb; in still other cases the inflorescence develops first, and the leaves and pseudobulb only develop after the flowers are over; finally, there are cases in which the leaves and pseudobulb of a flowering branch remain rudimentary, never developing beyond a size of a few millimetres. In the last case, a bud from the base of an old pseudobulb may do one of two things: it may either grow into a rhizome ending in a pseudobulb and leaves, without flowers; or it may grow into a rhizome ending in an inflorescence, without developed leaves or pseudobulb.

Among Malayan species of Coelogyne, a common lowland species called *Coelogyne Rochusseni* has this last habit (Fig. 26*b*). It has slender limply pendulous inflorescences each bearing numerous cream-coloured flowers; the pseudobulbs are rather tall and slender, not bulb-shaped, and the leaves are short and broad. Other well-known cultivated Malayan species of Coelogyne are *Coelogyne asperata* (Fig. 26*a*) and *Coelogyne pandurata*, the former with cream flowers and brown warts on the lip, the latter with green flowers and black warts on the lip. Both these species have inflorescences which develop before their pseudobulbs and leaves. Attempts to cross *Coelogyne asperata* and *Coelogyne Rochusseni* have failed; perhaps a compromise between the two growth-habits is impossible.

The genus Cymbidium is widely distributed in tropical Asia,

Leong Hong Stra

FIG. 26—(a) *Coelogyne asperata*: young leaves just appearing from sheaths at base of inflorescence × ⅓; (a¹) column and pollinia of *C. asperata* × 2; (b) *C. Rochusseni*: part of inflorescence × ⅓; the leaves at the base remain rudimentary and do not emerge.

and includes some very fine species which grow on the mountains of Burma and have been much used for hybridizing in Europe. These species and their hybrids cannot be grown satisfactorily in the lowlands of Malaya, though they flower well at Cameron Highlands. We have, however, some interesting lowland Malayan species. A Cymbidium plant has a sympodial growth, each new stem consisting of a short pseudobulb bearing several leaves, the sheaths of which normally quite cover the pseudobulb. The leaves of our common species are long and rather narrow, thick and leathery; they are jointed near the base. Inflorescences are pendulous, each with many flowers (Fig. 27a). The sepals and petals are cream to greenish with a purple median band, the lip white with purple and yellow markings. The column is fairly long, and the pollinia are removed from it by insects in the usual way. There are two pollinia, both seated upon a single crescent-shaped "disc". This differs from Coelogyne, in which there is a viscid mass but no distinctly formed disc of tissue.

Related to Cymbidium is the giant orchid called Grammatophyllum. If you imagine each pseudobulb of Cymbidium greatly elongated, bearing leaves all along its length, the leaves thin instead of thick, and the inflorescence erect with larger flowers, you have *Grammatophyllum speciosum*. The "pseudobulb" of Grammatophyllum commonly reaches five to six feet in length, and may attain double this. The giant plants often grow in the crowns of large trees, sometimes very high above the ground; in such cases the pseudobulbs (which begin by growing erect) bend and hang down in graceful curves. The roots have a special character; they are slender, stiff, and much-branched, and grow upwards and outwards (Fig. 27b). Dead leaves and other debris are caught by this mass of orchid roots; by the decay of this material the orchid obtains necessary food, and the decaying material also absorbs water during rain (thus forming a store of water *outside* the plant, not within it as in a pseudobulb). The pollinia of Grammatophyllum are almost identical in appearance to those of Cymbidium.

Another genus of the same alliance is particularly interesting. It is called Dipodium, and includes two well-known species and at least one other which is apparently less common in

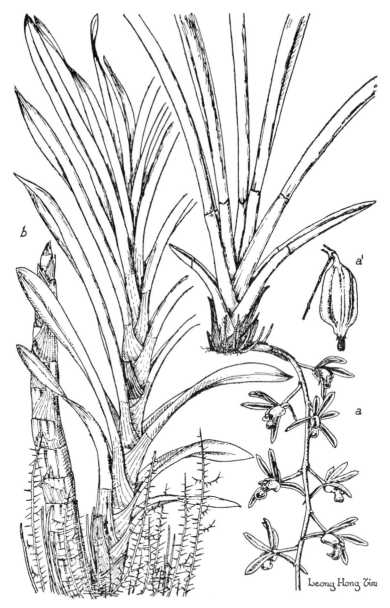

Leong Hong Lim

FIG. 27—(a) *Cymbidium pubescens:* base of plant with part of inflorescence; (a¹) fruit × ½; (b) *Grammatophyllum speciosum:* part of a young plant × ½.

Malaya. The stem and leaves of Dipodium are quite like a single stem (or pseudobulb) of Grammatophyllum; but in Dipodium this stem has acquired the habit of bearing roots above the base (Fig. 28a). Stems of *Dipodium pictum*, which climb up small trees in moist shady forest, have therefore acquired the growth-habit of Vanda (see Chapter 3), but the related Grammatophyllum has not. A Grammatophyllum "pseudobulb" never bears roots above the base, and though it may go on growing at the tip for a long time it is not unlimited in growth as in Dipodium. Dipodium shows what an easy step it is from the sympodial to the monopodial state; it is only necessary for the stem to acquire the habit of bearing roots at intervals throughout its length, and the apex of the stem acquires the power of unlimited (monopodial) growth. One is tempted to think that the Vanda tribe and the Cymbidium tribe may have had a common origin, as they are the only tribes (apart from Vanilla, which is very remote) which have acquired the monopodial habit.

The Vanilla of commerce consists of the fruits of a Mexican orchid. The fruits are fleshy and contain rather large seeds. The almost ripe fruits are picked and fermented, after which Vanilla essence can be extracted from them. (The same substance is now more cheaply produced synthetically.) It is interesting to note that the scent of Vanilla is found in many other quite different orchid genera (e.g. in *Dendrobium leonis* and *Eria pannea*). There are native species of Vanilla in Malaya also, but their fruits do not produce the same fragrance. Vanilla plants are like Vanda in having acquired the power of unlimited growth, but they differ from Vanda in bearing roots only at the bases of the leaves; one root to each leaf, and no more (in Vanda there may be two or more roots near the axil of a single leaf, but not all leaves have adjacent roots). The climbing stems of Vanilla form a very interesting pattern, with alternate obliquely descending fleshy leaves and a root opposite the base of each (Fig. 28b). Malayan Vanilla flowers are quite large and showy, but are apparently not common, though the plants may be quite abundant. The commercial Vanilla has less showy flowers; it grows well in Singapore island, but needs a regular dry season to flower well. In the north of Malaya is a pretty little Vanilla in which the leaves are reduced almost to nothing, and the

FIG. 28—(*a*) *Dipodium pictum*: top of a climbing plant × ½; (*b*) Vanilla: part of a climbing stem × ½; (*c*) *Calanthe veratrifolia*: single flower × 1½.

Leong Hong Tim

active part of the plant is the green fleshy stem; this is called
Vanilla aphylla.

Related to Vanilla, and with the same habit of growth as
Vanilla aphylla (i.e. with very small leaves) is a very curious
genus called Galeola. Galeola plants are pinkish-brown in
colour and have no chlorophyll, so they cannot make carbohydrates for themselves from the carbon dioxide of the air.
They are therefore dependent on other plants for their food, but
they are not direct parasites. They live on decaying organic
matter (often on the stump of a dead tree) but they cannot absorb
their nourishment direct. The intermediary is a fungus, which
causes decay of the dead wood, etc., and absorbs the decomposition products. Thus in Galeola the adult plant has continued
throughout its life the dependence on a fungus shown by young
seedlings of all orchids. A Galeola plant climbs by means of
roots, one opposite each leaf, exactly as in Vanilla, and may
climb to a height of fifty feet. It must thus abstract a great deal
of food from its fungus partner, and one wonders whether the
fungus has any service in return. A plant like Galeola is called
a saprophyte (*sapros* means decaying), because it lives on decaying material of other plants. There are also other saprophytic
orchids; they are mentioned in Chapter 14.

Two terrestrial orchids, Arundina and Spathoglottis, have
been mentioned in Chapter 3. There are many other terrestrial
orchids, mostly confined to shady forest; some of them are not
at all common or do not flower freely, and doubtless more
remain to be discovered. The genus Calanthe has some twenty-
five species, and is interesting because it includes both evergreen
and deciduous species. All the native Malayan species, except
two which are only found in the north, are evergreen plants of
moist shady forest. They have leaves rather like Spathoglottis,
and are in fact related to Spathoglottis, but part of the lip is
joined to the column (forming a tube) and the base of the lip
is produced backwards into a slender tube or spur containing
nectar. The commonest species (*Calanthe veratrifolia*) has pure
white flowers and is often cultivated (Fig. 28c), and there are
some very beautiful yellow-flowered species in mountain forests.
Two deciduous species grow in the north; they have large pseudobulbs which store water and tide the plant over the dry season,

the leaves then falling completely. Inflorescences grow from the bare pseudobulbs before the new leaves appear. The nature of the stimulus causing this seasonal flowering after the resting stage is not established. Another terrestrial genus with plicate leaves is Plocoglottis. The flowers of some species, notably *Plocoglottis Lowii*, have a curious arrangement by which the lip springs up against the column when suitably touched (Fig. 29, b, b^1, b^2). The lip is actually pushed downwards by the petals during the opening of the flower, and then is held in position by one lateral sepal, after which the petals move to their normal places. At a touch, the lip springs up into contact with the column and remains there. This must be an elaborate pollination mechanism, and would serve to press an insect into contact with the pollinia, which it might remove in its efforts to get free; but no insect has been observed to do this. *Plocoglottis Lowii* grows in rather wet lowland forest, most commonly in Pahang and Johore.

The response of the Pigeon orchid to a temperature stimulus is not an isolated case. Several other species of Dendrobium behave in the same way, but none of them are as common as *Dendrobium crumenatum*. Some flower only eight days after the stimulus of cooling, some ten or eleven days. In almost all cases the flowers last only a day. A similar response by short-lived flowers is shown by species of the genera Thrixspermum and Taeniophyllum (both of the Vanda tribe) and Bromheadia, all belonging to quite different branches of the orchid family from Dendrobium. It seems likely that some of these do not respond to quite the same stimulus as the Pigeon orchid (perhaps in some cases to a slighter stimulus), and differences in structure of inflorescence may also affect the nature of the response. More observations on these orchids are needed.

A very curious case is *Bromheadia finlaysoniana*, one of the commonest terrestrial orchids of open country throughout Malaya (Fig. 29, a, a^1, a^2). The flowers open at dawn and only last a few hours. Each inflorescence and each bud grow continuously, but there are some days with many open flowers, some with none. Observation has shown that dry weather (and probably also other unfavourable conditions) retards, but does not stop the growth of flower-buds at a certain stage of develop-

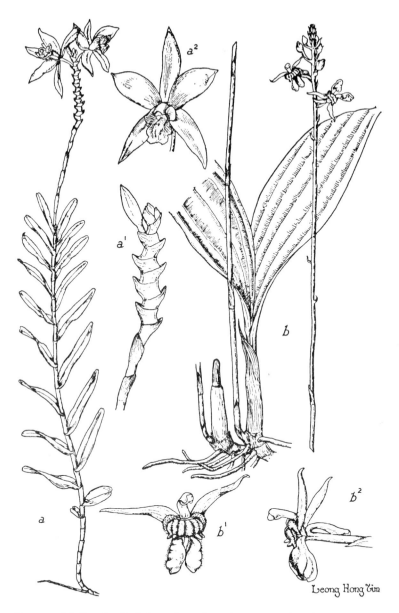

Leong Hong Yim

FIG. 29—(a) *Bromheadia finlaysoniana:* flowering stem × $\frac{1}{4}$; (a^1) inflorescence × 1; (a^2) a flower × $\frac{3}{4}$; (b) *Plocoglottis Lowii:* flowering plant × $\frac{1}{2}$; (b^1) front of flower, lip held down by right sepal × 1; (b^2) side view of flower × 1.

ment; normal development is resumed after an unusually cool day, and the flowers open on the seventh day following. While some buds are being retarded in growth, others (not yet at the sensitive stage) may catch up with them, and so all will flower together. Again, the gregarious flowering has a twofold significance: it follows a cool day, which in practice means a rainy day (so that the plants will be full of water for the development of flowers), and it ensures the simultaneous opening of many flowers, so that there will be a good chance of cross-pollination. Not only orchids respond to such a stimulus. Coffee bushes do the same; also the giant Angsana trees (*Pterocarpus indicus*) and the fragrant Kĕmuning (*Murraya exotica*). At Penang there are many avenues of fine Angsana trees. In the dry weather of the early part of the year these trees lose their leaves; then the inflorescences are formed on the new growth before leaves are developed. One morning about that season you may go out and see almost every Angsana tree covered with a sheet of gold, and the whole air is full of their scent. Next day all the flowers fall to the ground like golden rain. The inflorescences are rather small; each has twelve to twenty flowers. The first few buds of a young inflorescence grow to about half their full size, and then stop growing. When the next cool day comes, or the next sudden storm on a hot day, the buds are stimulated to further growth, and they open on the third day following. The next lot of buds on the inflorescence then repeat the process. Each inflorescence may flower in about three flushes; not all inflorescences may be simultaneous in development, nor all trees, but the major flowerings in Penang are large. In Singapore, trees are much less regular in their time of leaf change, and some may change leaves on one branch at a time, so that the flowering is usually much less spectacular than at Penang (and in any case there are fewer trees, as many died of disease about 1918–28).

One of the most remarkable cases of gregarious flowering is that of Keng Wah, a member of the cactus family commonly grown in Malaya; the botanical name is *Epiphyllum oxypetalum*. Keng Wah is a legendary Chinese name, but the plant is native in tropical America; it was, however, introduced to Singapore from Amoy (about 1920) and so was thought to be a Chinese plant. Perhaps it reached Amoy via Honolulu and Manila, but that is a guess.

A Keng Wah plant consists of narrow, flat, leaf-like objects, each of which has a notched margin. The flat objects are in fact stems, and tiny leaves can be seen at the notches of an actively growing stem. When a stem is well grown, small buds appear in the marginal notches. The buds grow until they are about 3 mm. long, and then cease growth. An exceptionally cool day is the stimulus to further activity; if it does not come within a few weeks, the buds shrivel and fall. On receiving a stimulus, buds at the appropriate stage begin to grow. Growth is at first slow, but it accelerates greatly. From 3 mm. long to nearly 300 mm. (the length at flowering) takes twenty-four or twenty-five days, and the greatest increase of growth in a single day is considerably more than an inch.

When full-grown, the flower-bud commences to open about 9 p.m.; it is fully open at about 10.30, and withers at dawn next morning. The actual stimulus to opening of the flower is, therefore, different from that of the Pigeon orchid which opens at dawn. Exactly what makes the Keng Wah open at night is not known. But the response to coolness (i.e. to rain) and the result in gregarious flowering are the same as in Dendrobium. The remarkable difference is that in Dendrobium a flower-bud is fully formed as regards all its essential parts (the pollinia fully developed) before it rests, whereas in Keng Wah the resting bud is so small that it must have the inner parts in a quite rudimentary stage of development.

CHAPTER ELEVEN

NEST-FERNS AND THEIR NEIGHBOURS

FERNS share with orchids a large part of the possible living-room for epiphytes in Malaya. There are some 500 known species of Malayan ferns, and at least half of them are epiphytes. Ferns have a quite different way of life from orchids, and they show different methods of detailed adaptation to the problems of water and food-supply, but the same basic principles are seen at work in both groups of plants. Orchids have developed larger and more specialized water-storage organs, but some ferns have evolved a humus-collecting mechanism much more efficient than that of any orchid. Ferns are often pioneers, preparing the way for orchids. Ferns and orchids are alike in the extremely delicate and vulnerable nature of their early stages of growth, and it is astonishing that with such handicaps both groups have become so successful. The ferns which are most remarkably adapted to epiphytic life are the nest-ferns, and we will consider them first.

The common nest-fern is called *Asplenium nidus* (Fig. 30a). It is to be seen on almost any old tree anywhere in Malaya. Each plant consists of a nest or basket formed from a number of simple broad ascending fronds, and beneath the nest an erect stem bearing many spreading roots. The top of the stem, which produces new fronds from time to time, is in the bottom of the basket. Dead leaves falling from the tree which bears the fern are caught in the basket of fronds, and these accumulated leaves, which slowly rot, form a covering for the top of the fern stem. In due time, the top of the fern stem produces a crop of new fronds; these grow at first vertically upwards through the decaying debris, and then bend backwards, holding the decaying material firmly between their bases and the bases of the next preceding fronds. Roots then grow from the stem outwards through the decaying mass, which helps to feed them. Even-

142

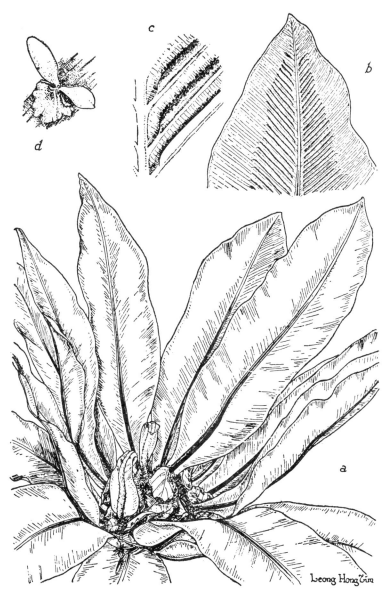

FIG. 30—*Asplenium nidus:* (a) looking into the basket, young fronds growing up among litter of dead tree-leaves × ¼; (b) tip of frond × ½; (c) midrib and bases of 3 sori × 2; (d) young plant growing from prothallus × 2.

tually, the old parts of the stem of the nest-fern are covered with a large mass of spreading roots, each with a woolly covering of root-hairs, growing in a mass of decaying leaves and old frond-bases. This mass of material forms a sponge which will hold a large quantity of water. After a heavy rain, the sponge is full, and beneath it may be trickles of water which supply the needs of other plants. The spongy mass of a nest-fern's roots is also often used as a rooting-place by other plants (chiefly ferns).

The total surface area of the fronds of a single nest-fern is considerable, and though the plant has a better reserve of water than most epiphytes, the fronds could not exist unless they had good protection from rapid loss of water. They are, in fact, very tough, and wither slowly if plucked. On the lower side of most of the fronds are dark lines which extend obliquely from either side of the midrib halfway or more towards the edge. Examination with a lens shows these lines to run along the veins, and each line to consist of a narrow translucent flap with many small brown objects beneath it (Fig. 30, *b*, *c*). The small objects are *sporangia*, and to see their structure clearly one needs the low power of a microscope. When the sporangia are old, they break open and shed microscopic *spores* which are borne away by the wind. A succession of new sporangia replace the old ones for a few weeks, and each frond of the fern sheds thousands of spores daily during the period in which its sporangia are ripening. The sporangia are so constructed that they break open when the air is dry, and the method of opening ejects the spores forcibly away from the sporangium.

All ferns are propagated by spores, which are wind-dispersed. As a large number of spores are produced, there is a good chance that some of them will be blown on to suitable places on the bark of a tree where they can germinate. But a spore does not grow directly into a new fern plant. It grows first into a small thin plate of green cells, called a *prothallus*. The prothallus bears, on its lower surface, the sexual reproductive organs of the fern. In order that fertilization may take place, a film of water must be present, as the male cells swim freely to the female (egg) cells. Each egg-cell is situated at the bottom of a small tube which projects from the surface of the prothallus; a male cell must enter the tube to effect fertilization. The united cell so formed (called a *zygote*) at once begins to divide and grow into a new fern plant, taking nourishment in its early stages from the prothallus (Fig. 30*d*).

Both prothallus and the very young fern plant which grows from it are very delicate and have no reserves of water. They therefore need a sheltered place or a continuous supply of water, at least for a few weeks. Water also is needed for the fertilization process. Ferns vary in the degree of shelter needed by their prothalli, and the amount of drought their young plants will stand. The nest-fern is evidently more resistant than some, but even so a spore must find a sheltered spot away from direct sunlight, or a place where there is a fairly constant trickle of water from an old nest-fern, or some other unusually favourable place for its germination, if a new plant is to be established. In countries with a seasonal climate, fern spores can only germinate in the wet season, which must be long enough for a new young plant to become established.

All ferns, whether epiphytic or terrestrial, pass through this prothallus or sexual stage. The places where ferns can grow are, therefore, limited by the needs of the prothallus; and spores of different kinds of ferns must be adapted to live under particular circumstances. A nest-fern spore, for example, would not grow on the ground, which would be a quite unsuitable place for the growth of the adult plant. The spore of a terrestrial fern which is confined to very shady places would not grow in the crown of a tree, where a nest-fern spore might grow quite well.

The other principal type of nest-fern in Malaya is the Stag's-horn fern called *Platycerium coronarium* (Fig. 31). This is found throughout Malaya except in the extreme north, where it is re-placed by another species of the same genus. Stag's-horn ferns are so called because of the shape of their fertile fronds, which in the Malayan species are pendulous; in an African species how-'ever they have the position as well as the shape of a stag's antlers. Malayan stag's-horn ferns have fronds of two kinds, one kind growing upwards and the other limply pendulous. The erect fronds have main veins repeatedly branched, but the fronds themselves do not consist of narrow branches as do the pendulous ones. The erect fronds form the nest, and catch dead leaves like

L

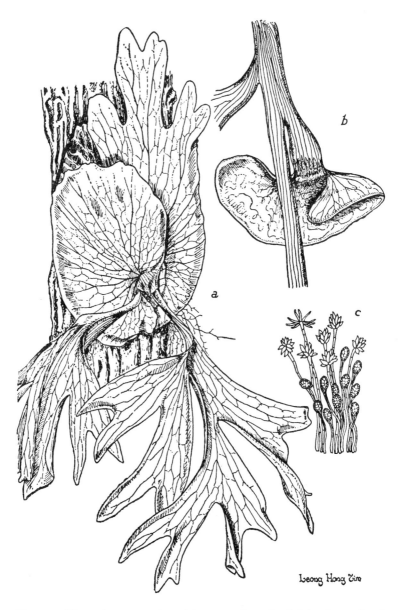

Leong Hong Tin

FIG. 31—*Platycerium coronarium:* (*a*) young plant, the left-hand nest-frond
half grown × ¼; (*b*) fertile lobe of old frond × ¼; (*c*) sporangia and their protecting hairs × 10.

the nest of *Asplenium nidus*. But when a nest-frond of Platy-cerium grows old, it curls inwards and thus holds within itself the mass of dead leaves it has accumulated. This mass of material protects the roots of the fern, which grow into it. Each successive nest-frond does the same, so that the top of the plant consists of dead and decaying nest-fronds with decaying tree-leaves between them. New nest-fronds are produced outside the old ones by the stem of the fern, which grows slowly outwards, away from its supporting tree. The decaying mass of a Platycerium is a water-sponge just as in Asplenium; it is a more efficient one, as the roots are totally enclosed by the decaying nest-fronds.

The pendulous fronds of *Platycerium coronarium* may be six feet long, with many branches. When they are old, they are shed (as the nest-fronds are not). The pendulous fronds have special stalked semi-circular lobes near the base, and these lobes bear sporangia crowded on the lower surface; the sporangia are embedded in a mass of felted hairs, which protect them when young (Fig. 31c); when the felt breaks up, the spores are dispersed.

Old Platycerium plants often have another curious fern grow-ing out from the lower surface of their outer nest-fronds. This fern (called *Ophioglossum pendulum*) has limply pendulous nar-row ribbon-like fronds (Fig. 32a). Some of these fronds, on a well-grown plant, will be seen to have curious slender cylindrical lateral appendages; these have sporangia embedded in them, and in due time the sporangia open and liberate spores. These spores are dispersed by wind, but they have no power to germinate into green prothalli like most fern-spores. If such a spore is blown into the nest of a Platycerium plant, it settles among the decaying leaves and soon finds itself completely covered. Under these circumstances it germinates, but being in the dark, it cannot produce chlorophyll; lacking this, it can only grow with the help of fungus. If the right fungus is present, and if it infects the growing fern-spore, the fern-spore can take food from the fungus, which in turn can take food from the decaying leaves in the nest of the Platycerium. So the prothallus lives at the expense of the Platycerium's food-store, through the inter-mediary of the fungus. When it is large enough, the prothallus produces sexual organs, and after fertilization a new Ophio-

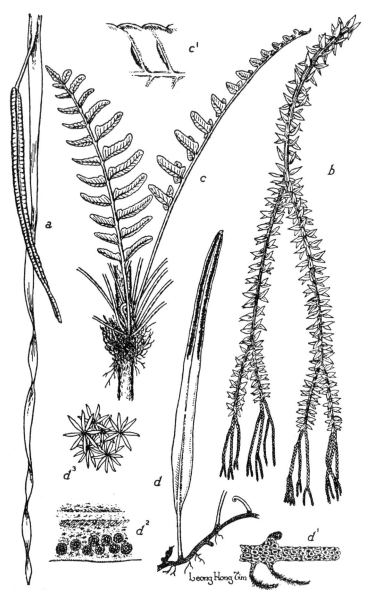

Fig. 32—(a) *Ophioglossum pendulum:* a leaf with spike near base × ½; (b) *Lycopodium phlegmaria* × ½; (c) *Asplenium tenerum* × ½; (c¹) sori of c × 2; (d) *Pyrrosia adnascens:* rhizome bearing fertile leaf × ½; (d¹) rhizome × 1½; (d²) sori × 3; (d³) hairs from young frond × 30.

glossum plant begins to grow. This plant must at first live at the expense of the prothallus and its fungus, as it can have no green fronds until it comes to the light. When the first frond of Ophioglossum reaches the light (which it does by growing downwards), it turns green and begins to make its own food like any other green leaf. But still the Ophioglossum plant is dependent on the Platycerium for its water-supply, which is that held by the sponge in the Platycerium nest. It seems that as the Ophioglossum plant grows larger, it eventually absorbs so much water that it prevents active growth of the Platycerium, and finally the Platycerium dies and leaves a large bunch of pendulous fronds of Ophioglossum hanging from its decaying nest. Such a plant must have a limited life; I have no idea how long it could last after the death of the Platycerium. But I have always noted that really large Ophioglossum plants are only found on dying or dead Platycerium plants.

The prothallus of Ophioglossum is a saprophyte; it lives in the same way as the young seedlings of orchids, and also in the same way as the curious orchid called Galeola (Chapter 10). There are other plants besides ferns which have saprophytic prothalli, the most important being species of Lycopodium. The commonest Lycopodium sometimes forms thickets on very poor abandoned ground which will not support other plants. A Lycopodium plant looks like a small fir tree, and has little pendulous cones on its branches. In the cones are sporangia, one to each small leaf, and the spores germinate to produce partially saprophytic prothalli, which grow on earth banks and have little green lobes. They are very difficult to find. But there are also epiphytic species of Lycopodium, mostly pendulous, with larger leaves than the terrestrial one (Fig. 32b). These all have totally saprophytic prothalli, which presumably grow in crevices of decaying bark and similar situations; they do not grow on Platycerium plants, though sometimes in places where they may participate in the water draining from the nest of a Platycerium or an Asplenium.

There is a near relative of *Asplenium nidus* which also has a nest, though a much smaller one; this second species is called *Asplenium tenerum* (Fig. 32c). It grows only in rather moist shady forest, often on small trees near the ground, or sometimes on rocks. Its fronds are not simple, but each has a single row of leaflets on each side of the axis. The sporangia are again borne in rows along the veins, protected when young by a narrow flap or indusium (Fig. $32c^1$); this is a character of all species of Asplenium, some of which have a quite different habit of growth. *Asplenium tenerum* develops a mass of roots with decaying debris, like that of *Asplenium nidus* but smaller; the roots bear very copious brown root-hairs. Other species of Asplenium have pendulous fronds which cannot form a nest; and some have a creeping rhizome. Some of these live on or near the nests of the nest-forming species.

The young leaves of Platycerium are covered with a web of interlacing star-shaped hairs. These hairs help to protect the young fronds from drying. There is another genus of ferns, with slender creeping rhizomes and simple fronds, but with similar stellate hairs, which is considered to be related to Platycerium. This genus is called Pyrrosia (it has also been called Cyclophorus). Several species are very common in rather exposed places on old trees everywhere in Malaya (Fig. 32d). These ferns have fleshy fronds which store water, and when young (even in some cases when old) they are very well protected by the felt of star-shaped hairs, at least on the lower surface. The sporangia (which have no protective indusia) grow also under the shelter of the felt of hairs, breaking through to the open air when they are ripe. The fronds of Pyrrosia are jointed to the rhizome and fall when old. The rhizome itself is not very large; it is protected by overlapping scales, much like the scales of a snake. These ferns are often found in association with mosses, which are perhaps the pioneers and help to collect some humus which can be used by the roots of the ferns both as a source of food and water and as a protection from the sun. The very common Drymoglossum is a near relative of Pyrrosia. It has almost round sterile fronds, the fertile fronds being elongate with a band of sporangia along the edges.

Some epiphytic ferns grow especially on old palm trunks of the kind which do not shed their leaves neatly. The old leaves of a Kabong palm, for example, break near the base, and leave the bases themselves surrounding the trunk. Each leaf-base has many black fibres, and these, with the decaying leaf-base itself, provide excellent shelter for the growth of fern prothalli. The same kind of thing is true of an Oil palm, but this has no black hairs on its leaf-bases. A fern which is very common on such old palm trunks is *Davallia denticulata* (Fig. 33a). This has a creeping rhizome nearly as thick as one's finger (thus able to store some water) covered with brown scales. The fronds are rather widely spaced on the rhizome, and are deeply dissected. On the small ultimate leaflets are the groups of sporangia (called *sori*), in little pockets at the ends of some of the veins, close to the edge on the lower surface. There are several other species of Davallia in Malaya; all have scaly rhizomes with widely-spaced fronds, and sori of similar general form, though differing in detail. An old palm trunk covered with Davallia plants is very decorative, but perhaps is not considered good by the people who have to manage Oil palm estates. With the Davallia also may be other smaller ferns.

Besides the true nest-ferns, there are others which have special protective and humus-collecting fronds, though these do not form a nest. The commonest of such ferns belong to the genus Drynaria, of which two species are often abundant on old trees in all parts of Malaya (Fig. 33b, c) and a third occurs in the north. Drynaria plants have a stout scaly rhizome, which bears fronds of two kinds, persistent and deciduous. The persistent fronds are unstalked, short, and broad, with prominent main veins each ending in a lobe on the margin. These fronds commonly overlap each other and almost cover the rhizome and its roots; they soon turn brown and persist until they decay with age. They collect some humus, but a far smaller quantity than the nest of Asplenium. The other fronds are stalked, long, deeply lobed, and they bear sporangia in small round groups in a pattern on the lower surface. These fronds are green throughout their life, and are shed like the leaves of a tree when they are old. There are fine Drynaria plants on some of the large Rain trees at Kuala Lumpur.

In mountain forests are other ferns which have fronds of only one kind, combining the function of the two kinds of fronds of Drynaria. The commonest of these ferns is called *Algaomorpha heraclea*. The fronds may be up to six feet long; they have very broad entire bases which protect the rhizome and roots and

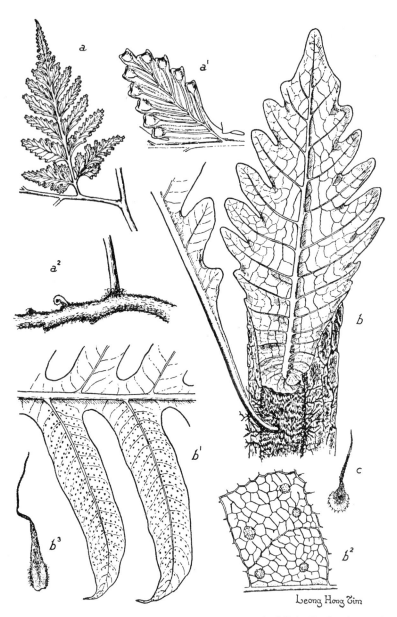

Leong Hong Tim

FIG. 33—(a) *Davallia denticulata*: part of frond × ½; (a¹) leaflet bearing sori × 2; (a²) rhizome × ½; (b) *Drynaria quercifolia*: rhizome, bearing nest-frond and base of a green frond × ½; (b¹) part of green frond × ½; (b²) venation and sori × 3; (b³) scale from rhizome × 3; (c) *D. sparsisora*: scale from rhizome × 3.

collect humus, while the upper part of the frond is deeply lobed and bears sporangia in the same way as a Drynaria. It is probable that Aglaomorpha shows a stage in the evolution of Drynaria from ferns with uniform simple fronds, and one Malayan fern with such fronds has just the characters one would expect of such an ancestor.

Drynaria and Aglaomorpha have a very interesting pattern of venation. The veins form a network of small meshes, and in the meshes are short free veinlets pointing in all directions. This venation pattern is characteristic of most of the near relatives of the genus Polypodium. Polypodium itself, based on a temperate-zone fern, has a simpler but derivative form of venation; I think that it represents a reduced, specialized condition, not the primitive form of the family. It is interesting that *Polypodium vulgare* is the only epiphytic fern in Britain; it is a stray member of a tropical family, doing its best to maintain tropical habits under difficult conditions.

In Malaya there are a number of members of the Polypodium family, besides Drynaria and Aglaomorpha. Most are smaller than Drynaria, and some much smaller. They all have creeping scaly rhizomes with fronds jointed to them, and most have round unprotected sori. Some, however, have the sori in oblique lines, between the main veins. Many have leathery fronds that do not allow the characteristic vein pattern to be seen, but it is there all the same. A few of these ferns have ant-inhabited rhizomes (see Chapter 16).

In mountain forests, on mossy trees, there are a number of small ferns which are more or less covered with reddish hairs. The sori of these ferns are round and unprotected, for which reason they have been called Polypodium, but it seems probable that they belong to a quite different family. Those with entire fronds are called Grammitis; those with lobed fronds are mostly placed in the genus Ctenopteris. This family of small epiphytic ferns is distributed throughout the tropics, mainly on mossy trees in mountain forest. I believe them to be highly specialized and reduced, not primitive.

The most delicate of all Malayan epiphytes are the filmy ferns. These grow only in places where the atmosphere is saturated with water-vapour a large part of the time; they are most abundant in mountain forest.   The fronds of most ferns, like the leaves of flowering plants, have internal air-spaces, which communicate with the outer air by means of tiny openings called stomata.   But the fronds of filmy ferns are only one cell thick (except for the midribs) and so cannot have an internal atmosphere.   Just as they easily lose water by evaporation from the whole surface of a leaf, so they can also absorb water through the whole surface.   They are often dripping wet for long periods. They respond to dry weather merely by shrivelling, and have the ability to withstand a moderate degree of drying for a limited period (probably not more than twelve hours; they would always be wet by dew at night).   Such ferns can only exist in the most moist and shady places in the forest; in the lowlands they are only found beside small streams.   They are usually grouped in two genera, Hymenophyllum and Trichomanes, but some recent authors subdivide Trichomanes into several separate genera.   The smallest filmy ferns have fronds only a few millimetres long; the largest are rarely over a foot long.

The sporangia of filmy ferns are borne at the tips of the narrow ultimate branches of the fronds.   They are either in funnel-shaped depressions, or protected by two more or less triangular flaps, or by both methods.   The sporangia are of somewhat primitive structure, and the family is believed to be an ancient one, though it does not compare in antiquity with our common Rĕsam ferns.

CHAPTER TWELVE

TERRESTRIAL FERNS

PROBABLY the commonest fern in Malaya is that known by the Malay name Rěsam, and to botanists as *Gleichenia linearis* (Fig. 34*a*). This (with its varieties or near allies) forms dense long-persistent thickets in open places and is probably the most difficult form of vegetation for the human pedestrian to penetrate. Gleichenia is sometimes called bracken, but it is a very different fern from true bracken; the only character they have in common is that of forming thickets.

Gleichenia is interesting to botanists as one of the more primitive genera of ferns. Before I ever came to Malaya, I saw fossil Gleichenias in cretaceous rocks in West Greenland, where no doubt they formed thickets long before man existed; and they are known from much earlier rocks. Their primitive character is reflected in their large and curiously formed sporangia, which are few in number and simultaneously produced on any one frond-branch. Anatomically also, Gleichenias show primitive structures.

A Gleichenia plant has a slender creeping and branching rhizome, which grows along the surface of the ground and roots at intervals (Fig. 34*a*³). The rhizome also bears the stalks of fronds, and each frond continues growing for a considerable time. One plant, derived from a single spore, may thus ultimately form a thicket. The fronds have a character shared by few other ferns. Each frond bears a succession of pairs of lateral branches, and while each pair of these branches develop, the top of the frond ceases from growth. When the pair are complete, the main axis of the frond resumes growth until it has produced another pair of branches, during the development of which it again rests. The tip of the main axis of each frond thus spends most of its time as a resting bud.

In forest clearings and beside paths on Penang Hill, and on

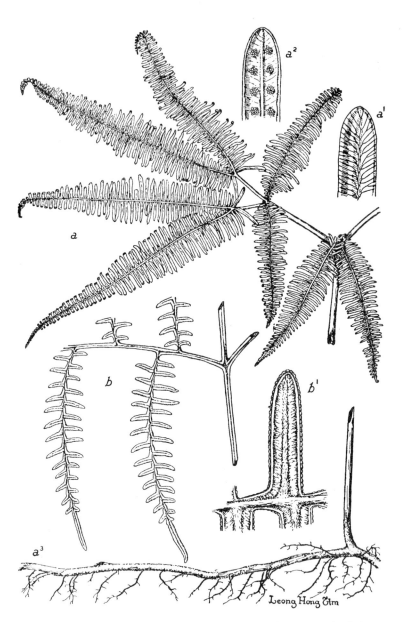

Leong Hong Tim

FIG. 34—(a) *Gleichenia linearis:* part of frond × ¼; (a¹) upper and (a²) lower surfaces of a leaflet × 6; (a³) rhizome × ½; (b) bracken: part of frond × ½; (b¹) under surface of leaflet × 4.

other hills of similar and greater altitude in Malaya, is another kind of Gleichenia which also forms thickets. This mountain Gleichenia has the same habit of resting the bud of the main axis while each pair of frond-branches grow, but each frond-branch itself grows to completeness, without forming any further resting buds. The lowland Gleichenia carries the resting habit to much greater lengths. Each frond-branch grows for a time and then again forms a pair of secondary branches with a resting bud between them; each of these secondary branches then repeats the process. Sometimes the pairs of branches formed are unequal, and alternate inequalities make a distinctive pattern. The ultimate pattern is in any case a series of equal or unequal forkings which are formed because a bud in the fork becomes dormant. Normally these dormant buds, apart from the bud at the top of the main axis of the frond, remain always dormant. An unequal forking of this kind, with development of dormant buds, is also found in the genus Lygodium, mentioned below, but not in the near allies of Lygodium. It is a specialized branch-system which has developed on a few distinct lines of evolution among ferns.

The ultimate leaflets of Gleichenia have small free veins, and on the lower surface of some of the veins are small round groups of sporangia, without any indusium. The spores find suitable growing places on sheltered bare earth banks where there is not much direct sunlight, and young plants, growing from prothalli, are often very abundant. As above noted, one such young plant can ultimately form a thicket, and can spread far from its starting-point.

Gleichenia plants demand light. If trees grow up around them, the shade of the trees will ultimately weaken or kill the Gleichenia. But Gleichenia thickets, when well developed, are so dense that trees can rarely establish themselves from seeds in the thickets. The result is that open places in forest often become filled with Gleichenia thickets which may persist through long periods. But destruction of the thickets is not difficult, though it may be laborious. The Gleichenia rhizome is slender and on or near the surface of the ground. If the fronds are all cut down and removed, the rhizomes and their shallow roots are exposed to the heat of the sun, and this is sufficient to kill most of them; thereafter trees can be established which will ultimately prevent further growth of the fern. If the Rěsam is burnt, it will be completely killed, but burning is not always desirable or practicable.

In this vulnerability to cutting and fire, Gleichenia differs markedly from true bracken (Pteridium), which also exists in Malaya (Fig. 34b). Bracken has a much stouter rhizome which is quite underground, and so is both better protected against sun and fire and also provided with a better reserve of food to start new growth if the fronds are destroyed. The result is that cutting or burning bracken does not kill it unless several times repeated at short intervals. Bracken, like Gleichenia, is a light-demanding fern, but it does not normally compete with Gleichenia, because the two have different soil preferences. Bracken will only grow in a rather well-drained soil, and Gleichenia grows on clay.

Bracken fronds have pairs of branches like Gleichenia, but there are no resting buds. The two ferns also differ greatly in the way in which their sporangia are produced. The leaflets of bracken have narrow reflexed edges, and the sporangia grow under the protection of these (Fig. 34b¹). There are two species of bracken in Malaya, one mainly on the mountains (but also in Singapore) and the other always in the lowlands; the latter is the southern type, and the former rather like that found in Europe, but more hairy.

As noted above, there are Gleichenia thickets, of various species, on the mountains. On a limited number of isolated mountain summits (not only the highest) there occurs another fern which forms thickets, though less dense than those of Gleichenia. This fern is called *Matonia pectinata* (Fig. 35a). It is abundant on Mt. Ophir, Gunong Tahan, and Kedah Peak; on the Main Range it is less abundant, probably because it is adapted to very poor acid soils where most other plants will not flourish. In the Cameron Highlands district it has only been found on G. Těrbakar. Matonia fronds have branches which are quite like the ultimate branches of a Gleichenia, but their arrangement is peculiar. At the top of the leaf-stalk, the first branches diverge in a V, with no bud between them (the branching is called a true dichotomy). The next branches diverge on

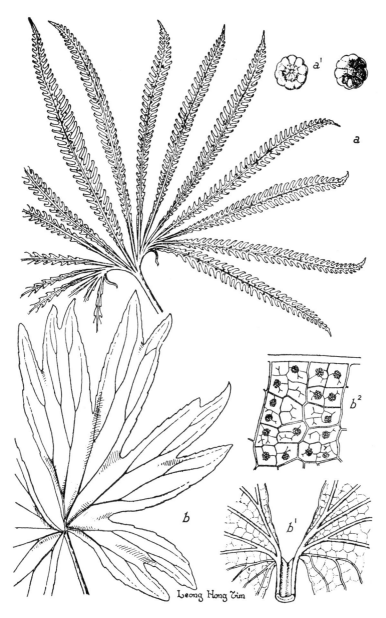

FIG. 35—(a) *Matonia pectinata:* frond × ⅛; (a¹) sori × 6; (b) *Dipteris conjugata:* part of frond × ¼; (b¹) base of frond × 1; (b²) detail of veins and sori × 6.

the outer sides of the first pair, near their bases, and the process is indefinitely repeated. The result is a fan-shaped frond of peculiar pattern. Like Gleichenia, Matonia is interesting because it is a primitive fern, and fossils of its near relatives have been found in many parts of the world. Today Matonia is found only on mountain tops in Western Malaysia, with a single nearly related genus extending from Borneo to New Guinea. This relative (Phanerosorus) has a different frond-habit, resembling Lygodium on a smaller scale. Matonia is perhaps the nearest thing to a living fossil among native Malayan plants.

On Penang Hill and elsewhere at moderate elevations, there grows another fern of open places which in some ways resembles Matonia. This fern is called *Dipteris conjugata* (Fig. 35*b*). It has a frond like two wings (whence the name Dipteris), and the branchings of the main veins in the two halves of the frond form the same pattern as the branching of a Matonia frond. A Dipteris frond is, in fact, like a webbed Matonia frond, with a complex netted venation of the Polypodium family pattern. It is considered that Dipteris is a primitive ally of Polypodium, representing perhaps a stage of evolution through which Polypodium has passed. Again, fossils of near allies of Dipteris have been found in many remote parts of the world (including Britain). Dipteris is found in Singapore island, in scrubby vegetation on sea-cliffs in a few places, but elsewhere in Malaya it does not normally grow at much less than 2,000 feet altitude. It has a stout rhizome which grows near the surface of the ground. On Penang Hill, Dipteris is very freely reproduced from spores, but I have seen few young plants in Singapore. Can the Singapore plants be a relic of a time when the climate of Singapore was cooler?

Botanists always pay special attention to primitive ferns, because of their evolutionary interest, and it so happens that such ferns are well represented in Malaya. Some of them, like Gleichenia, are also of interest because of the distinctive part they play in local vegetation. We will refer next to a few more such ferns.

Wherever you may walk in open country in Malaya, you will not go far before seeing a plant of Lygodium, which has very curious slender, much-branched climbing fronds (Fig. 36*a*).

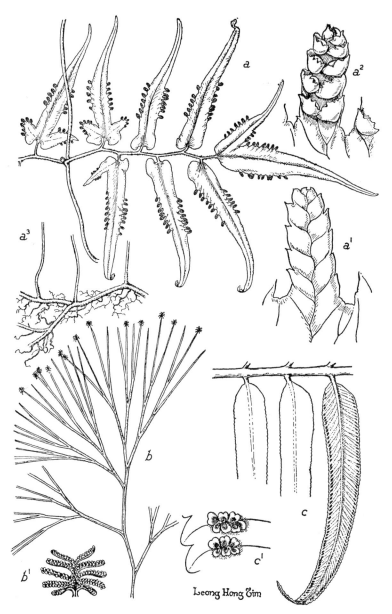

Leong Hong Tim

FIG. 36—(a) *Lygodium flexuosum:* part of frond × ½; (a¹) fertile lobe upper
surface and (a²) lower surface × 8; (a³) rhizome of *L. microphylium* × ½; (b)
Schizaea dichotoma: part of frond × ½; (b¹) tip of a branch × 5; (c) *Angiopteris:*
part of one branch of a frond × ½; (c¹) sori × 8.

M

They climb by twining round other plants. A young Lygodium plant has fronds which do not climb; they branch by a series of almost equal forkings which make a pattern rather different from that of Matonia, but based on the same scheme. In later fronds, by a series of unequal forkings, the climbing habit develops; it is in part based on the formation of dormant buds like those of *Gleichenia linearis*, but arranged differently. The sporangia of Lygodium are arranged on small lobes along the edges of some of the leaflets (the blade of which is narrower than the blade of sterile leaflets). There are four common Malayan species of Lygodium, two always found in sunny places, scrambling over shrubs, and two in more shady places.

A much less common fern is *Schizaea dichotoma* (Fig. 36b). The fronds of this are much like those of a young plant of Lygodium, but with more forkings and narrower branches. A common species of Schizaea is often found in rubber estates and other moderately shaded places. Though common, it is not conspicuous, because it has narrow grasslike fronds which bear a few slender, brownish fertile lobes at the tip.

A fern which probably belongs to an even more ancient family than Matonia is not uncommon near streams in Malayan forests. It is called Angiopteris (Fig. 36c). Its fronds are very large, and the base of the stalk of a frond may be as thick as one's arm. Angiopteris is not a tree-fern, though its fronds are often larger than those of any tree-fern. It has no trunk, but only a very massive stem which is more or less hemispherical in shape, the old parts of it covered with the bases of former fronds. The leaflets are fairly large, the veins free, and the sporangia in coherent groups arranged along each vein near its end.

In northern latitudes the Royal fern, *Osmunda regalis*, is justly famous for its beauty; and roots of Osmunda are widely used as a substratum for the culture of orchids. The Osmunda family is also an ancient one. In Malaya we have one species (Fig. 37a), which is widely distributed in south-east Asia and Malaysia, but in our country it is probably confined to mountain valleys in the northern part of the Main Range. It was not known to occur in Malaya until about 1934, when I found it in a small valley near Renglet at Cameron Highlands. It is rare in the main Bertam valley at the Highlands, but very abundant

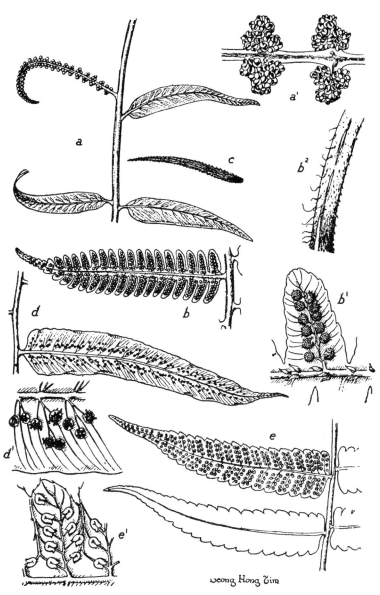

Leong Hong Lim

FIG. 37—(a) *Osmunda javanica:* part of frond × ½; (a¹) old sporangia × 4;
(b) *Cyathea latebrosa:* leaflet × ¾; (b¹) one lobe of leaflet × 3; (b²) base of leaf-stalk × ½; (c) scale from *Cyathea squamulata* × 4; (d) *Cyathea brunonis:* leaflet × ½; (d¹) part of leaflet × 2; (e) *Cyclosorus sumatranus:* part of frond × ¾; (e¹) part of leaflet × 3.

in the Telom valley, near the river at 4,000 feet altitude, grow-ing along with the pretty *Anemone sumatrana* and a little violet. The Royal fern has tall bipinnate fronds which have sporangia on the upper branches only; our Malayan *Osmunda javanica* has simply pinnate fronds, with some fertile pinnae near the middle of each frond. The sporangia are large and the spores have an astonishing green colour. Though the fern grows naturally at about 4,000 feet altitude in forest, it can be grown satisfactorily in Singapore, though perhaps it would not regenerate here from spores. It has to a limited extent a curious character, found in some other ferns, of developing a mucilaginous covering on its very young fronds. This is described below in connection with the genus Cyclosorus.

Tree-ferns are a characteristic feature of mountain landscape in Malaya, especially where forest has been felled near streams. The common large tree-fern needs a good light for vigorous growth, and is not found in deep forest shade, but some other kinds of tree-fern are only found in the depths of the forest. The habit of growth of a tree-fern has been described in Chapter 2. All tree-ferns are alike in this, and all must begin to grow from a prothallus, which needs a moist sheltered place for its develop-ment. Probably prothalli of different kinds respond to different light intensities, and this may in part explain the groves of *Cyathea contaminans* (the largest of our tree-ferns) in open places.

The tree-ferns of the world belong to two families, Cyatheaceae and Dicksoniaceae. The former family has much the larger number of species, and all our dozen kinds of Malayan tree-ferns belong to it. Dicksonia is mainly distributed in the southern hemisphere. One species occurs on the mountains of Borneo and Sumatra at about 7,000 feet altitude; it has not yet been found in Malaya, and perhaps our mountains are not high enough to give it the right climatic conditions.

A characteristic feature of Malayan tree-ferns is the covering of scales on the very young fronds, when they are coiled up at the top of the trunk. These scales also persist more or less on the bases of the fully grown fronds. The structure of the scales is characteristic for each individual species, and the first step in identifying a tree-fern is an examination of the scales with a hand lens (Fig. 37, *b*, *c*). There are smaller scales on the rest of the frond, and these sometimes show other characters, but a high magnification is necessary to see them clearly.

Cyatheaceae is one of the more primitive families of ferns, as judged by the structure of the sporangia and the fact that the sporangia in one sorus develop in a regular sequence. But it is a family that seems to be in process of active evolution, judging from the great variety of species found throughout the tropics. In a recent survey of the family in Asia, the Malayan region and the Pacific, about 270 species are distinguished. Many of them are superficially very much alike, and one needs to examine scales and indusia carefully to distinguish one species from another. All are placed in one genus, Cyathea. Formerly the family was divided into three genera on the basis of the indusium, but this division proved quite artificial. One can find two ferns alike in every character except presence or absence of an indusium, and it is both artificial and unpractical to place them in separate genera. Fig. 37, *b*, *b*¹ show part of the commonest lowland tree-fern, which has no indusia; Fig 37, *d*, *d*¹ show a smaller species which has indusia.

There are a considerable number of very ordinary-looking terrestrial ferns, both in the forest and in open places, which belong to the genus Cyclosorus and its near allies (Fig. 37*e*). All these ferns have simply pinnate fronds, with lobed pinnae and small round sori covered (in most species) with round or kidney-shaped indusia. At first sight these ferns look very much alike, but on close inspection it will be found that they differ in venation, degree of lobing, hairiness (kinds and distribution of hairs), shape of lowest and uppermost pinnae, and in other characters. Some species only grow in the forest, some always in the open, some always in swamps, some only on the mountains. Some of these ferns have a double row of very small leaflets on the stalks of the fronds. Usually there is a small swelling behind the base of each of these small leaflets. It seems fairly clear that this swelling is an aerating organ, as loose tissue here comes to the surface. In a few of these ferns, these swellings are elongated and have the appearance of small spur-like outgrowths. Their significance is seen when the fronds are very young. At this stage, when the fronds are in the shape of very small coils, their surface is covered with a thick layer of slime. The aerating organs are white, and they project through the slime, which otherwise prevents access of air to the young fronds. It has been suggested that the slime is a method of protecting the young fronds from drying. But ferns which have this character are only found in quite moist conditions, where they are in no possible danger of drying. My opinion is that the slime (which is actively excreted by certain cells) is a method of getting rid of excess water which would not be lost by evaporation in the ordinary way, because the air is so humid. A plant needs to absorb a certain amount of water in order to absorb also certain necessary dissolved substances from the soil; without these substances (containing nitrogen, phosphorus, etc.) the plant cannot build up the living substances of new fronds.

Tectaria is a genus of terrestrial forest ferns which have elaborately netted venation and round sori. In different species the fronds have different shapes; in one they are simple and entire, in others simply pinnate, in others double pinnate. Tectaria illustrates a tendency which occurs in various fern genera, namely the loss of indusia. Once a sorus has lost its indusium, a second tendency appears, for the sporangia to spread along the vein instead of being in a small circular patch. This spreading can be seen in a common lowland forest species called *Tectaria maingayi* (Fig. 38a), which still grows in the forest of Bukit Timah in Singapore. Slightly spreading sori can also be seen in a less common species (also at Bukit Timah) called *Tectaria barberi*. Why ferns lose their indusia is not clear, but there are certainly many instances of the loss, on many different evolutionary lines. Presumably some other sufficient method for the protection of the young sporangia is developed. Or it might be that in moist shady forest such protection is unnecessary. In some species of the Cyclosorus alliance which have no indusia, the sporangia themselves are covered with stiff hairs, which perhaps afford some protection; such hairs are not found on sporangia which are protected when young by an indusium.

A number of species of terrestrial forest ferns, with the habit of Cyclosorus, have sori running along the veins, somewhat as in Asplenium (Fig. 38b). These ferns are called Diplazium (they

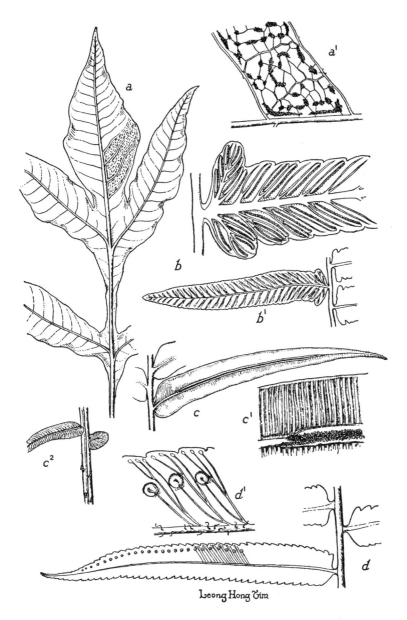

Leong Hong Gim

Fig. 38—(a) *Tectaria Maingayi*: top of frond × ½; (a¹) venation and sori × 4;
(b) part of Diplazium leaflet, showing sori × 2; (b¹) whole of same leaflet × ¾
(c) *Blechnum orientale*: leaflet × ½; (c¹) part of leaflet × 2; (c²) base of frond ×
½; (d) *Nephrolepis biserrata*: leaflet × ¾; (d¹) part of leaflet showing sori × 3.

are also called Athyrium). Some of them have very large fronds, as long as those of a tree-fern and of similar appearance, but they are quite distinct in their sori, and in their scales. Scales are an important diagnostic feature of all kinds of ferns, but a micro- scope may be necessary to distinguish details of their structure. A genus called Blechnum is mainly found in the southern hemisphere, though one representative (*Blechnum spicant*, the Hard fern) reaches Britain. In Malaya, *Blechnum orientale* is a very common fern of open places (Fig. 38*c*). It has pinnate fronds with entire pinnae; young fronds are pink. Below the pinnae and all down the stalk of the frond are very numerous small round leaflets. On the base of each leaflet is a small gland, which is not in the same position as the breathing organ of Cyclosorus. It has been suggested that these glands excrete water, but I have never observed this, and think that they also may be breathing organs. But some other ferns, including Platycerium, and also many flowering plants (e.g. the Castor Oil plant and the African Tulip tree) have liquid-excreting glands on their young leaves, and the liquid is usually sweet. These glands are called extra-floral nectaries. They are some- times visited by ants, which consume the sugary liquid, but it seems hardly likely that their prime function is to nourish ants. It is possible that they help to excrete unwanted water, but no decisive investigation of their function has been made.

There is a fern genus called Nephrolepis, which has two very common Malayan species. They sometimes form thickets, grow- ing on the ground, and they can also grow in the old leaf-bases of Oil palms. Some related species are always epiphytic. The fronds of Nephrolepis are borne in close tufts, and the spread- ing is done by means of slender runners which arise laterally on the short erect stems which bear the fronds. Each frond is pin- nate, and bears many closely placed leaflets at right angles to the axis. The tips of the leaflets are pointed and curve upwards. The veins are free, and the sori, near the edge, are round (Fig. 38*d*[1]). The sori are much like those of Cyclosorus in shape, but it is improbable that the genera Nephrolepis and Cyclosorus are nearly related.

Some seventy years ago, at Boston in America, a cultivated Nephrolepis plant produced a runner which bore very finely dissected fronds instead of simply pinnate ones. The freak plant was propagated, and is now cultivated in many parts of the world, including Malaya, as a "Lace fern". There is a good deal of variation in the degree of division of the lace fronds, and sometimes a new runner will bear fronds of the normal simply pinnate form. It is thought that all primitive ferns were finely divided, and the lace ferns of Nephrolepis may thus represent a reversion to a more primitive leaf-form. This is of some interest in relation to the peculiar juvenile leaf-forms of Teratophyllum mentioned below.

There are some ferns which only grow on rocks in stream beds in shady forest. Of these, the most interesting belong to two related genera, Bolbitis and Egenolfia (Fig. 39a). These genera agree in having sporangia-bearing fronds of very different form from the sterile fronds. The leaflets of fertile fronds are very narrow, and the lower surface of each is completely covered with sporangia; such fronds also have longer stalks than the sterile fronds. This form of fertile frond is called acrostichoid, because it was first noticed in the genus Acrostichum, described below. The acrostichoid condition (seen also in the fertile lobes of Platycerium fronds) has evidently arisen on several different evolutionary lines among ferns. In the early schemes of fern classification, all acrostichoid ferns were placed in one genus, but in view of their great dissimilarity in other ways, and in view of the clear relationship of some of them to various distinct fern genera, the old genus Acrostichum is now broken up into its constituent parts, and the name is confined to the original species and its near allies. Bolbitis and Egenolfia, however, are two very closely related genera, one with netted veins and one with free veins. The netted venation of Bolbitis has led to a condensation and simplification of the frond-form of some species, but other species have fronds like Egenolfia. It seems likely that a hybrid between the genera has been produced in a valley in Bukit Timah, Singapore, where a potential parent species of each genus grows on granite boulders. The suspected hybrid has never been found anywhere else. In both genera the rhizome creeps on the rocks, adhering by roots, and bears closely placed fronds in two rows, alternately, on its upper surface.

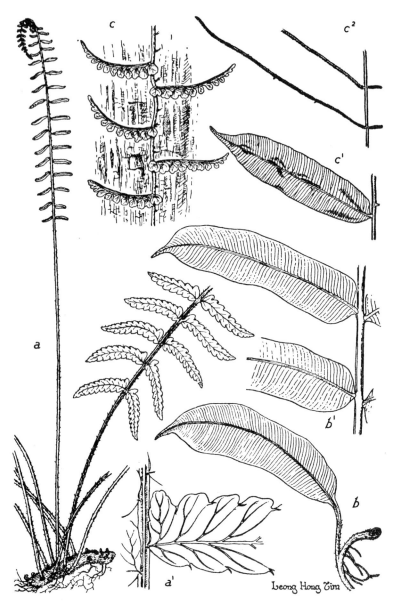

FIG. 39—(a) *Egenolfia:* plant, showing whole fertile frond and part of sterile one × ¾; (a¹) part of sterile leaflet × 2½; (b) *Lomariopsis:* young plant × ½; (b¹) part of frond of older plant × ½; (c) *Teratophyllum:* young plant climbing tree-trunk × ¾; (c¹) sterile leaflet from old plant × ½; (c²) fertile leaflets × ½.

There are two very remarkable genera of acrostichoid climbing ferns which in my opinion are related to Bolbitis. The genera are called Teratophyllum and Lomariopsis, and in the past they have been confused with a third genus called Stenochlaena, because all have a similar frond-form. Stenochlaena, however, differs greatly in anatomy, in spores, scales, and other characters, from the two genera first mentioned; it is a common fern and is described further below.

Lomariopsis plants (Fig. 39b) start life as prothalli on the ground in shady forest, or on the roots of trees close to the ground. They develop a rhizome which may at first creep on or near the ground, but eventually climbs a tree trunk. It climbs by means of roots which adhere to the bark of the supporting tree, but it has also water-absorbing roots in the ground. The rhizome eventually may climb fifty feet or so above ground-level, bearing many spreading fronds which are simply pinnate. The pinnae of these fronds are jointed to the axis, and when old they fall. They may also fall in dry weather, when they would be an embarrassment to the plant owing to their too great loss of water. As a result of the stimulus of dry weather, fertile fronds are from time to time produced. These fronds are also simply pinnate, but the pinnae are very narrow and are completely covered beneath with sporangia. The veins of Lomariopsis are free. There is a related genus called Lomagramma which has closely similar fronds with netted veins; it differs also from Lomariopsis in starting life, like Bolbitis, on wet rocks by forest streams, not on the ground or on tree-roots, though eventually the plants of Lomagramma climb trees like Lomariopsis.

Teratophyllum also has high-climbing rhizomes that start on or near the ground, pinnate fronds with jointed pinnae and free veins (Fig. 39c), and fertile fronds with narrow pinnae (Fig. 39c^2). It is peculiar in bearing on young plants fronds which are unlike those on mature plants, and differ somewhat from species to species (Fig. 39c). In general, these peculiar fronds are much more finely dissected than those on mature high-climbing rhizomes. But this "juvenile" state is also produced by branches of older plants which are near the ground, and it appears to be a response to the weak light and great humidity of the lowest stratum of the forest. I have called these fronds *bathyphylls* (leaves of low level), and I believe they are an indication that the ancestors of Teratophyllum had more deeply dissected fronds. A more remarkable development of such fronds occurs in some species in the region of the New Hebrides. Teratophyllum plants are only found in very moist and shady primitive forest. Fertile fronds are not common in Malaya, and are only borne by plants which have high-climbing rhizomes. Their development is certainly a response to dry weather. Dry weather means less water-supply for a high-climbing plant; the fertile fronds have less surface to lose water by evaporation, and they need dry air to ripen sporangia and disperse spores.

Stenochlaena palustris is a common fern in rather wet ground in sunny or lightly shaded places (Fig. 40a). It often forms thickets, as it has a long creeping rhizome. Like Lomariopsis and Teratophyllum, it ultimately climbs trees, and like them also it has simply pinnate fronds and narrow acrostichoid pinnae on fertile fronds. Its young fronds are pink and succulent; they are sometimes eaten as a vegetable. Stenochlaena may be distinguished from the other climbing ferns (apart from its more open habitat) by the toothed edges of its leaflets. It has glands on its leafstalks as in Blechnum, but not quite of the same shape, and their function is uncertain. As with Teratophyllum, the fertile fronds are produced in response to dry weather, but it usually happens in Singapore that the dry weather is all over by the time the fertile fronds actually appear.

In open places in mangrove forest grows a very tall fern which I believe is related to Stenochlaena, though some other botanists do not agree. This fern is the original Acrostichum, and the smaller upper pinnae of many of its fronds are covered beneath with sporangia (Fig. 40b). The fronds may be six feet or more tall. The lower pinnae are quite broad, with a finely netted venation; when young the fronds are pink, as in Stenochlaena, and they have also glands on their stalks. Acrostichum plants sometimes form thickets when the trees of mangrove have been felled, and they are regarded as a troublesome weed by foresters, because young trees cannot grow in an Acrostichum thicket. There are two distinct species of Acrostichum in Malayan mangrove, one with smaller fronds and pointed leaflets,

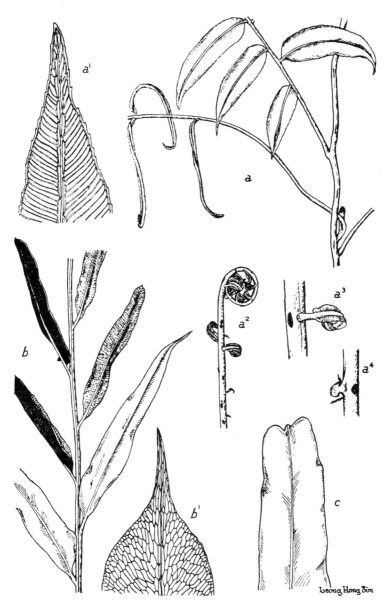

Fig. 40—(a) *Stenochlaena palustris:* climbing stem with parts of sterile and fertile fronds × ½; (a¹) tip of sterile leaflet × 1½; (a²) very young frond × ¾; (a³) base of young leaflet; (a⁴) gland-bearing reduced leaflet × 2; (b) small *Acrostichum:* part of top of frond × ½; (b¹) tip of sterile leaflet from b × 1½; (c) tip of leaflet of the large *Acrostichum* × ½.

the other with taller fronds and blunt leaflets (Fig. 40, *b*, *c*). The former grows in more saline places, and the latter may sometimes be found persisting in wet places in land reclaimed from mangrove which is no longer at all saline. The Malay name for Acrostichum is Piai.

CHAPTER THIRTEEN

CLIMBING PLANTS

THE Malayan forest is rich in climbing plants, many of them so large that they can reach the tops of the tallest trees. Such large climbers (or lianes) must have woody stems, and these rope-like objects, sometimes of fantastic shape, are almost everywhere a feature of the forest. The Malays use the word akar, which means a root, for the leafless pendulous stems of these climbers. There are also smaller climbers, many of them attached to tree trunks by their roots; and there are twining or scrambling climbers, of small or moderate size, which abound on the edges of forest, often making access to forest difficult. Besides these, there are many garden climbers, some cultivated for their flowers, some because of their useful products (e.g. yams, see Chapter 4).

A single plant of a large climber may intermingle its foliage with that of a tall forest tree, spreading its branches throughout the crown of the tree. It may, in fact, have about as many leaves as the tree itself. It uses the support of the tree to bring its leaves and flowers to the sunlight. By doing so, it dispenses with the need to make a thick woody trunk for itself. But as it has as many leaves as the tree, it also needs to transport as much water to them as the trunk of a tree carries to its own leaves. As mentioned in Chapter 2, water travels from roots to leaves of a tree through small tubes embedded in the wood. These tubes are called *vessels*; they consist of rows of large cells the cross-walls between which have disappeared. In a cross-section of a tree trunk, the vessels are seen to be scattered through the wood. Most of the wood is made of firm fibrous tissue; it must be strong enough to support the crown of the tree, and it could not do this if it consisted only of vessels. But this does not hold true for climbers which use the tree for support. So the xylem (wood) of a climber can (and usually does) consist almost entirely of vessels (Fig. 41a). Thus a cross-section of a climber will show as many vessels as a cross-section of a tree trunk many times its size.

One result of this is that the concentrated stream of water in a climbing stem can be used by a thirsty traveller when he needs a drink. If you cut a length of three or four feet from a large climbing stem, and hold it vertically, water immediately drips from the lower end in sufficient quantity to be caught for drinking. After the dripping has ceased, more water can be extracted from the lower end by cutting a piece from the upper end. The water is always safe for drinking. It has not passed through the living cells of the plant, and these alone might contain poisonous substances; the vessels are quite devoid of living substances, and merely serve to pass on the water from the earth which has been absorbed by the roots.

When a climber has reached the crown of a tree, its branches cannot go higher, but they do not stop growing. As they grow, the older part of the stem slips downwards, the small leafy twigs retaining their level. Thus the thick base of an old climber may rest in coils on the floor of the forest. This creates further problems. The stem must be more or less flexible; it must also be able to bend without disturbing the water stream by making kinks in the vessels. Different climbers solve these problems in different ways. Among the most remarkable are the species of Bauhinia. In these there is no solid cylinder of wood, but cambium is formed at various centres, the result being a series of separate strands, rather like the separate strands of a rope (Fig. 41b). Some other Bauhinias have a flat stem, varied by humps on one side and the other alternately (a hollow on the reverse side of each hump). Some species of Vitis (related to the Grape vine) have flat stems up to about six inches wide and no more than half an inch thick.

Woody climbers are produced by plants belonging to many families of dicotyledons. In a few families most members are climbers, but in most families some are climbers and some are not. Monocotyledon climbers are mostly much smaller than dicotyledons, because they have no cambium, but the Rotans, which are climbing palms, have stems as long as any dicotyledons, or even longer.

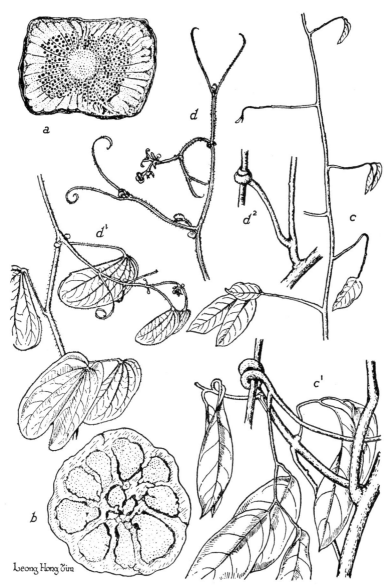

Fig. 41—(*a*) section of climbing stem of *Vitis*, showing water-channels × 2; (*b*) section of old stem of *Bauhinia*, showing separate strands of woody tissue × ½; (*c*) young stem of *Annonaceous* climber—one branch has bent in response to contact × ⅓; (*c¹*) older branch of same plant, showing grasp of support × ½; (*d*) climbing *Bauhinia*: tip of growing stem × ½; (*d¹*) older part of same × ½; (*d²*) fully developed hook × ½.

N

Dicotyledon climbers may be classified according to their means of support, as twiners, hook climbers, tendril climbers, and root climbers. In the family Annonaceae there are some species which seem to combine the first three classes, and they will be mentioned first. The family includes quite a number of medium-sized trees as well as the climbers. The flowers are very distinctive, with three sepals, six petals in two unequal whorls of three, many stamens, and many separate ovaries; the ovaries each form a separate fruit, so that one flower can produce a bunch of fruits. Annonaceae may also be recognized by their chambered pith; a longitudinal cut through the pith shows that it consists of cross-walls with hollows between them.

In a number of species of this family, the young main stems grow quite fast upwards and produce a good many small lateral branches almost at right angles, before the leaves are much developed (Fig. 41c). These lateral branches are sensitive to contact. If one of them touches any firm object, the side of the stem opposite the point of touching is stimulated to grow, whereas the touching side does not grow. If the object touched is a small branch of a tree, the young branch of the climber will thus grow in such a way as to make one or two turns round it. The part of the climber-branch which has thus got hold of a support then rapidly increases in thickness and becomes woody, thus strengthening its grip (Fig. 41c^1). Sometimes one of these small branches may coil round more than one support, making complex contortions, and sometimes the twigs of one climber-branch may become interlocked with the twigs of another. But one way or another the leading branch of the climber, growing upwards and bearing its sensitive and almost leafless horizontal twigs, usually makes enough contacts to support it and permit of further climbing. After the twigs have made their grip, their leaves begin to grow. A lot of leaves produced before the grip had been effected would prevent the sensitive twig gaining suitable contacts.

Twining climbers support themselves by twining round their supports. Here the whole stem keeps on twining as long as it is in active growth. The Annonaceous climbers only twine with special branches for a limited period. Their behaviour is more like that of a cucumber, which produces special slender branches called *tendrils*. The tendrils are sensitive to contact, and thus coil round possible supports, but they never bear leaves; they are more specialized than the branches of the Annonaceous climbers, which bear leaves eventually, whether they have effected a grip on other plants or not. The cucumber tendrils become slightly woody when they have coiled round their support, but never become much thickened. The Annonaceous climbers differ again by making fewer coils than the tendrils of a cucumber, and then making the one or two coils thick and woody. The coils, in fact, become grappling hooks specially fitted to their support. There are other kinds of climbers which bear hooks rather than tendrils, the hooks being special branches which are hooks and nothing else, without the power of bearing leaves. Tendril climbers and hook climbers are thus specialized cases of two processes which we see in less specialized form in the family Annonaceae. We can imagine that the ancestors of the cucumber had leaf-bearing tendrils; the modern tendril is more efficient and more specialized, and in becoming so has lost the power of bearing leaves; the same is true of some of the hook climbers we will next mention.

In the genus Artabotrys, of the family Annonaceae, only special branches have the power of forming hooks. These branches sometimes also bear flowers, and so they may be considered to be modified inflorescences (Fig. 42b). They do not, however, bear leaves. They grow in the axils of certain leaves, and these bear a special relation to the main branch; the hooks are thus in a certain pattern, more localized than in other members of the family. Each hook-branch is crook-shaped from the beginning, but it only becomes woody if it makes contact with something to which it can hold. The woody thickening then develops in such a way that the hook is eventually flattened, thus giving maximum strength for the amount of the woody material involved. In this genus, therefore, there is a more specialized support-mechanism than in most members of its family.

Hooks are found also in climbers of at least four other families, and they are in all cases modified lateral branches, which do not bear leaves. The hooks of different climbers differ a good deal in their size and thickness in their early stages, but all of them become woody and thickened as soon as they have become attached to a support. We will consider briefly those of Bauhinia and Uncaria.

The genus Bauhinia has been referred to above as having in some species a very peculiar method of secondary thickening, so that the woody tissue is in separate strands; the explosive fruits of Bauhinia, and their brilliant orange flowers, are mentioned in Chapter 7. The leaves of most Bauhinias are two-lobed, and the name itself commemorates two brothers named Bauhin, who were pioneer botanists in their day (more than three hundred years ago). But in some of our big climbing Malayan Bauhinias, the two lobes of the leaf are merged into one, and one must inspect the apex of the leaf very carefully with a lens to see the signs of its dual nature. When the leaves are young, they have stipules, which (as usual with such structures) develop before their leaves and protect the still younger leaves. Looking at an actively growing Bauhinia twig, with young undeveloped leaves and their protective stipules (which make an interesting pattern), one sees also many slender and beautifully curved hooks projecting from among the leaves (Fig. 41, d, d^1). Each hook is shaped rather like a question mark. If such a hook catches hold of a support, its curved end soon grows in such a way as to grasp firmly, and woody tissue is then developed; hooks which do not secure a hold soon fall. Even the woody hooks do not last as long as the woody coils of Annonaceae; they serve a temporary purpose, to be replaced by many more hooks on the later young twigs of the climber.

The genus Uncaria belongs to the same family as coffee and Ixora (Rubiaceae). There are about seventeen species in Malaya, and one of them is Gambier, formerly much cultivated for its tannin. All members of Rubiaceae have leaves in opposite pairs, and the stipules of the two leaves are joined together. If you find a climber with these characters, and a stout curved hook in the axil of each leaf of a pair, it is certain to be an Uncaria (Fig. 42c). One Uncaria is common in thickets on the edge of forest and in clearings. It has very stout stems, large hairy leaves, and spherical inflorescences each consisting of many small tubular radiating flowers; a leaf may thus have either a branch, or a hook, or an inflorescence in its axil. In a climber of another family (Roucheria) there may be an inflorescence and a hook in

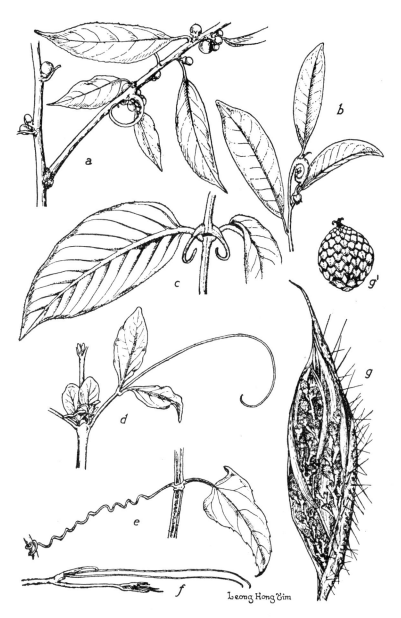

Leong Hong Gim

FIG. 42—(a) *Roucheria:* hook in leaf-axil × ½; (b) *Artabotrys:* hooked inflorescence × ½; (c) hooks of *Uncaria* × ½; (d) tendril of *Bignonia* × ½; (e) tendril of *Vitis angulata* = ½; (f) *Smilax:* tip of stem with tendrils = ½; (g) *Daemonorops:* inflorescence in spathe × ½; (g¹) single fruit × 2.

the same axil, but here the leaves are not opposite and the in-florescences are smaller (Fig. 42*a*). In Roucheria a hook is pro-duced in the axil of the first leaf on each lateral branch.

The cucumber is mentioned above as a tendril climber. A tendril is a slender clasping organ which curls many times round its support. In most cases also the basal part of the tendril (not involved in coiling round the support) also forms a coil which acts as a spring, so that a sudden gust of wind will not break the tendril. In some cases, however, tendrils are formed from the ends of leaves, and then the additional spring-coils are not always produced.

A common garden plant called *Bignonia* (or *Arrabidaea*) *magnifica* has leaf-tendrils. Each leaf has two leaflets, and its axis is produced beyond the leaflets into a slender slightly branched tendril (Fig. 42*d*). If the tendril does not gain hold of a support, it soon falls. A similar instance is found in the genus Entada, family Leguminosae, of which two species are native in Malaya. Here the leaves each bear a pair of pinnate branches and then the tendril. Entada plants have slender spikes of small mimosa-like flowers, followed by very large woody pods. In *Entada Schefferi* the pod is straight, up to thirty inches long and three inches wide; in *Entada spiralis* the pod is twisted into a spiral (one edge short, the other long) and breaks up when ripe, each part containing one large seed (the fruits of some species of Pithecellobium, which are trees, have a similar structure).

Normal tendrils, formed from modified branches, are found in the Vine, Gourd, and Passion-fruit families. The Vine family (Vitaceae) includes almost forty native climbing species in Malaya, some large and some small, a few quite common. The tendrils are opposite the leaves, not axillary; the inflorescences, when they appear, are in the same position. It seems that the tendril or inflorescence is really a terminal structure, the growth of the stems being continued by the bud in the axil of the apparently opposite leaf. The leaves of these vines are either simple or they may have three or more leaflets arranged in a palmate manner (like the fingers on one's palm). *Vitis angulata*, with arrowhead-shaped leaves, is common in secondary thickets, and has angled young stems which become rather flat when old (Fig. 42*e*). The genus Pterisanthes, the species of which are all slender climbers, has very curious, flat inflorescences, looking almost as if its flowers were growing out of a leaf (which usually turns red). The genus Vitis is now usually subdivided into several genera (Cissus, Parthenocissus, etc.). All species have quite small flowers; some have fruits as large as grapes but none are palatable. It seems that some tropical American vines have quite edible fruits, and crossing of these with true Grapes has been attempted. The parasite Rafflesia (see Chapter 14) grows on the larger members of Vitaceae in Malaysian forests.

The Gourd family, which includes the cucumber, pumpkin, vegetable marrow, wax gourd, bottle gourd, snake gourd, and the various melons, all climb by means of tendrils, which are axillary branches. In Malayan forests are large climbers belonging to several genera, the commonest being Trichosanthes, some of which have conspicuous bright-red egg-shaped fruits.

The yellow Buah Susu, though native in the American tropics, has become a weed in Singapore, scrambling over bushes and trees in secondary thickets, and climbing to a great height when it has opportunity. The small species called *Passiflora foetida*, with miniature passion-fruits surrounded by curious much-branched bracts, is also a weed, having been introduced as a cover crop. In tropical America, Passiflora is a large genus; in Malaya the family has few native representatives, the principal genus being Adenia, of which there are five species. Like the passion-fruits, these plants climb by means of slender axillary tendrils. They may be recognized from their bright-red fruits (in some species to three inches long), which have curious white-stalked pitted or warty seeds, displayed when the fruits open.

The family Apocynaceae includes the yellow Allamandas, native of tropical America, which are so common in our gardens, and in some cases have run wild in thickets near settlements. In the forests of Malaya are many climbers belonging to this family, some quite slender, some very large and woody; most of them have a white latex which exudes when any part of the plant is cut. The latex of some species of Willughbeia has been used as a source of rubber (Gĕtah Gĕrip), but it is now of no commerical importance. The same climbers have quite large fruits which contain a sweet edible pulp around the seeds. Most members of the family which are climbers twine round their supports, but in Willughbeia a different method is adopted. The leaves are in opposite pairs, and sometimes the stem beyond a pair of leaves becomes specialized as a sort of leafless tendril; in such cases, the buds in the axils of the two leaves grow into two new leafy branches, the stem thus forking where the tendril is formed.

Twining members of Apocynaceae include Chonemorpha (Gĕtah Gĕrip Merah), the species of which form very large lianes in our forests; they are also often cultivated in gardens, because of their large fragrant white flowers, which are borne in profusion. The flowers have a short tube bearing five large petals set obliquely, rather like the blades of a ship's propeller. In the related genus Strophanthus (known in Africa as a source of dart poison), the petals are produced into pendulous tail-like tips. Beaumontia is another genus of this family which has handsome large-flowered species often grown on pergolas. They are mostly native in the region just north of Malaya; the flowers are cup-shaped.

We have mentioned Bauhinia and Entada, of the great family Leguminosae, as climbing by tendrils and hooks. Other members of the family are twiners, and one of the most important is *Derris elliptica*, now largely cultivated because its roots produce a resinous substance called rotenone which is a valuable insecticide. Derris roots are called Akar Tuba in Malay, and they have been used from time immemorial as a fish poison for use on festive occasions. Fish are extremely sensitive to Derris poison, so that a very small amount is enough to stupefy them; the amount is far too small to affect their edible quality. Insects are far less sensitive to Derris root than fish, but even so the value of the fresh root as an insecticide is great. This use of Derris is quite recent, but its origin is uncertain; probably Chinese gardeners in Malaya were the first users. *Derris elliptica* is cultivated in open ground, and then is not allowed to grow into large plants. Related species in the forest grow into enormous lianes.

The family Rubiaceae, which includes the large hook-climbers called Uncaria, includes also some large twining climbers. One of these is a species of Morinda (Mĕngkudu), all members of which have a fine orange dye in their roots, similar to that of

Madder (Rubia) which gave the family its name. *Morinda umbellata* grows mostly in open thickets, but attains a large size. It is peculiar (like all members of its genus) in that the flowers are joined together in small heads, and the fruits also join together so that what seems to be one fruit is formed from the ovaries of several separate flowers (as in a pineapple and Nangka).

We now come to root-climbers. The principal plants which have this habit are the wild peppers (genus Piper), members of the Arum family (often called Aroids), and figs. There are also many others, including the climbing ferns mentioned in Chapter 12. Root-climbers rarely have thick woody stems. The Aroids are monocotyledons and have no cambium, so they cannot increase in thickness. The peppers are peculiar anatomically, and anyone might be excused for wondering if they were monocotyledons, especially in young stages, but they do form some wood eventually. Climbing figs can usually be distinguished by their white latex. The leaves of all these plants, when they are young and near the floor of the forest, usually lie flat against the supporting tree bark, but when they climb higher (like Teratophyllum) they develop leaves of a different kind which do not lie in this position. The Aroids sometimes ultimately appear to be epiphytes; but most of them retain contact with the ground, as noted below.

The true pepper, called *Piper nigrum*, is probably native in India. It is cultivated as a climber on posts some eight feet high, flowering on branches which grow away from the support. The flowers are in very dense small cylindrical spikes, and the fruits are small berries closely placed on the same, somewhat elongated, spikes. The wild peppers have more or less the same habit, but most of them live in the shade of the forest.

Some of the climbing figs also produce their inflorescences (the figs) on branches which grow away from the supporting tree trunk, but others do not. Among the latter is a conspicuous species called *Ficus callicarpa*, which has quite large figs of a beautiful orange colour, borne quite close to the tree trunk. One climbing Ficus is commonly planted to decorate walls with its small neat foliage; it is called *Ficus pumila*. When a plant of this kind reaches the top of its support, it produces quite large woody branches, which are quite different from the climbing stems, and with much larger leaves. On these spreading branches it also bears large green figs.

Climbing Aroids usually have two kinds of roots: slender roots which hold the plant to its supporting tree and grow more or less horizontally, and much thicker absorbing roots which grow downwards to the earth. The absorbing roots may hang freely in the air, like ropes, or they may run down the surface of the tree. In any case, they provide the large leaves of the plant, which are high above the ground, with direct access to the water in the soil. The lower parts of the stem of such a plant are then unimportant, and they may even die. The plant then looks like an epiphyte, but it remains rooted in the earth and so is in a very different condition from the truly epiphytic orchids and ferns. Some large Aroids also produce slender stem-branches which hang freely and grow downwards until they reach the earth, bearing only very small leaves. They then become creeping stems, with the power of climbing any tree they may meet. One such Aroid plant may thus in time produce stout leafy and rooting stems covering the trunks of a group of trees. A commonly cultivated species called *Raphidophora aurea* has done this in the Botanic Gardens, Singapore. This species was introduced to cultivation from the Solomon Islands in 1879, but its flowers were never seen until produced by a plant in Singapore in 1961.

The most important group of climbing monocotyledons are the Rotans or Rattan canes. They are palms, and they constitute a distinct type of woody climber, because, like other palms, their stems do not increase in thickness as they become older, and also because of the very numerous reflexed thorns on their leaves. Rattans belong to the same tribe as the Sago palm (see Chapter 2), and they are always tufted. Each new shoot bears at first a group of leaves close together, like any young palm, and then the stem begins to elongate rapidly, with a large gap (a foot or more) between each leaf-base and the last. The stems are then covered with the strong and usually thorny sheathing bases of the leaves. When the leaves are old, they and their sheaths wither and gradually rot away, leaving the stem or cane exposed. By this time the cane has become very firm, with a smooth hard skin.

Rattans climb by means of hooks. These are quite small, but

very numerous, and occur on the leaves and sometimes also on special branches which are borne in the same way as inflorescences. The hooks on the leaves are on the under side of the leaf-axis (or rachis) and sometimes also on a long whip-like continuation of the axis beyond its leaflet-bearing part (Fig. 50a[1]). The hooks are in little groups, are very short and stiff, and turned downwards. When each leaf is young, it stands erect at the top of its shoot. As it begins to unfold, it bends outwards, and in so doing it may come into contact with surrounding trees or other plants. The hooks hold firmly to any such support, and so the Rattan stem gradually climbs to the tree-tops. Rattans are so abundant in the lowland forest of Malaya that the whip-like thorn-bearing leaf-tips are a constant menace to the traveller.

A single Rattan stem or cane commonly attains a length of two hundred feet, which is about the height of the tallest forest trees. The longest cane ever measured in Malaya was about six hundred feet long. The canes (like normal palm trunks) are not branched. Because of their great strength and flexibility, Rattan canes have many uses, and they are therefore collected from the forest and form one of the most important minor forest products. As will be realized, they need the support of trees for satisfactory growth, and therefore they cannot well be grown in a plantation in the open; such a plantation would soon develop into a frightful tangle. There has been some cultivation of Rattans in Borneo, but in the main they are a product of native high forest.

Rattan canes vary a good deal in thickness, according to their kind. The thinnest are no thicker than an ordinary pencil, and the thickest two inches or more in diameter. The Malacca cane is one of the largest; it is known by the Malay name Rotan Sĕmambu. The walking-sticks prepared from Malacca canes consist of single internodes (that is, the length of stem between the attachment of one leaf and the next). Internodes long enough to serve as walking-sticks are not many, and they are only found on high-climbing parts of the cane.

There are considerably more than one hundred species of Rattans in the forests of Malaya, and many more in Borneo, Sumatra, etc. The largest genus is Calamus, with about seventy Malayan species; next comes Daemonorops with about forty.

These two genera are much alike in many ways, and though they are undoubtedly distinct, no single obvious character can be used to distinguish between them. Calamus on the whole have the longest canes and are most used, and some kinds of Calamus have long pendulous inflorescences, whereas the inflorescences of Daemonorops are always short (Fig. 42g). The most constant difference between the genera is seen in the bracts (spathes) of the inflorescences, which are tubular and persistent in Calamus, boat-shaped and deciduous in Daemonorops. The leaf-sheaths in both genera are often strongly armed with spines, the number and distribution of these being characteristic of the species.

The nature of these very close, tough, and persistent leaf-sheaths introduces the problem of the way in which an axillary bud, covered by such a sheath, can find room to develop. In various other monocotyledons which have tubular sheaths (including the Vandas and Scorpion orchids much cultivated in Malaya), the bud, whether of an inflorescence or of a new leafy branch, immediately pierces through the leaf-sheath, and so is free to develop further. This occurs in the Rattan genus Korthalsia mentioned below. But in Calamus and Daemonorops, perhaps because the leaf-sheaths are so tough, another solution of the problem has developed. Here the inflorescences do not first appear as axillary buds; they are in some way united with the leaf-sheaths, and an inflorescence grows out from the edge of a sheath, on one side of the base of the leaf-stalk. This is not known in any other group of monocotyledons. It is worth noting that in some other palms which have long leaf-sheaths, such as the Betel-nut (Pinang, or *Areca catechu*), the inflorescence begins to develop inside the sheath, which it distends somewhat, but does not fully expand until the leaf has been shed; the inflorescence then develops straight from the trunk, below the leaves, being in the axil of a fallen leaf.

The fruits of all Rotans, like those of the Sago palm, are covered with overlapping, smooth reflexed scales (Fig. 42g); these are formed from outgrowths of the wall of the ovary. Inside is the single seed, which is usually very hard. Many palms have hard seeds of ivory-like texture; the food-store in them consists mainly of cellulose. In the case of some species of Daemonorops, a dark red resinous substance is formed inside the scaly covering of the fruits. This substance is collected and sold under the name of Dragon's Blood.

The genus Korthalsia has seven species in Malaya, some of them quite common. They always have rather few and broadly triangular leaflets, and in addition may at once be distinguished by a tubular extension of the leaf-sheath above the insertion of the leaf-stalk. This extension (the *ocrea*) is often swollen and ant-inhabited (Fig. 50*a*, Chapter 16). Korthalsia, and also two other genera called Plectocomia and Plectocomiopsis, have the inflorescences all near the end of a stem, which is thus of limited growth, whereas the growth of a stem of Calamus is not so limited. In Korthalsia also the inflorescences are axillary, but immediately pierce through the bases of the leaf-sheaths in the axils of which they arise. Plectocomia has only one species, but the canes are very large, and the plants are common. When flowering, Plectocomia is a most striking sight, as the long pendulous inflorescences, all borne near the stem apex, bear large overlapping bracts, each of which encloses a group of flowers. These inflorescences grow normally in the leaf-axils and do not pierce through the sheaths.

Other forest climbers among monocotyledons (which have no secondary stem-thickening) are mostly much smaller than the Rattans. The true Yams (see Chapter 4) and Smilax, several species of each, are rather slender climbers more abundant along forest edges than under full shade, and unable to climb to the tops of tall trees. Both have broad leaves with three, five, or seven main veins from base to apex. Smilax may be distinguished from Dioscorea by having tendrils on its leaf-stalks (Fig. 42*f*); these tendrils are lacking in plants of Dioscorea, which climb by twining. Another common feature of Smilax and Dioscorea is that the plants are dioecious; that is, staminate and seed-bearing flowers are borne on separate plants. The fruits of Smilax are berries (usually orange) borne in clusters; the fruits of Dioscorea are three-winged capsules, often with rounded wings nearly an inch wide, and in each compartment of the capsule are round paper-thin seeds which are wind-dispersed. Much more observation is needed upon wild plants of both Dioscorea and Smilax in Malaya. They seem to flower rarely in the south of the country. As regards Dioscorea, the climbing stems die from time to time after fruiting (or sometimes perhaps without flowering or fruiting), but how often this occurs, and what obligate resting period is then undergone by the tubers, is in most cases not recorded, and may well vary in different parts of the country.

The genus Freycinetia, of the family Pandanaceae, includes very vigorous climbers. They are root-climbers, and so are festooned closely round the trunks and main branches of the supporting trees. They have very numerous close long and narrow leaves, like those of Pandanus but smaller. Freycinetias appear to flower rarely in Singapore. Male and female flowers are distinct, probably on separate plants. The flowers are densely packed together in club-shaped heads, and these heads are in the axils of brightly coloured leaf-shaped bracts. In some cases at least the bracts are fleshy and are eaten by squirrels. Unlike Pandanus, in which each compartment of an ovary has only one seed, Freycinetia has many small seeds in each ovary. Much more needs to be known about flowering of Freycinetia in Malaya; and it is not certain how many species we have.

CHAPTER FOURTEEN

PARASITES AND SAPROPHYTES

A PARASITIC plant lives by taking at least some part of its nourishment directly from the living substance of another plant. Some plants are wholly parasitic; they have no power of building up food material for themselves. That is, they lack chlorophyll, and so cannot use the sun's energy to synthesize carbohydrates; they must take advantage of other plants which can do this. Some other plants are partially parasitic. They have some chlorophyll, but in many cases lack roots; they then need to take some of the water (and salts) absorbed by the roots of other plants. The most important of these are the many members of the Mistletoe family.

A saprophyte is a plant that lives by decomposing the substances of other plants which are already dead. Saprophytic flowering plants thus lack chlorophyll, and in this agree with total parasites, though their methods of nourishment seem at first sight very different. When we examine the food-supply of such saprophytes, however, we find that they do not directly decompose the rotting material on which they live. The decomposition is done by a fungus, and the fungus in some way passes on at least part of the digested substance to the other plant. The fungus is thus the true saprophyte; the so-called saprophytic flowering plant is almost a parasite on the fungus. Fungi are by far the largest class among both parasitic and saprophytic plants. They are all totally devoid of chlorophyll, and have no alternative but to make use of the food-building work of green plants, either during the life of such plants or after they are dead. There are even fungi which are parasites on insects; the insects eat green plants and are then robbed of their substance by the fungi.

We will consider first some parasitic and saprophytic flowering plants; there are very interesting examples of both classes in Malaya. Then we will deal briefly with some fungi.

The most remarkable of all parasitic plants are the various members of the genus Rafflesia, found only in forests in Malaysia. They are parasites on woody climbers of the Vine family, attacking those parts of old climbing stems which trail along the ground. The first species known to Europeans was found by Raffles and Arnold in Sumatra in 1816. What they saw was a monstrous flower, a yard across, and some flower-buds, emerging from the stems of a vine. The species was named *Rafflesia Arnoldii*. Later another species was found in Java, a third again in Sumatra (it occurs also in Malaya), a fourth in Borneo, and a few more. Most of the others have much smaller flowers than the original species; that found in Malaya is about a foot across, but even so there are few other flowers which exceed it in size.

Rafflesia is not peculiar only in the great size of its flowers. It is the most specialized of all parasitic flowering plants, as it has neither stem, leaves, nor roots. Apart from its flowers, it consists of strands of tissue growing inside the living substance of its host, very much in the same way as a fungus grows, though differing, of course, in detail. A seed of Rafflesia germinates in a crack in the bark of one of the woody vines, and grows at once inwards. When it has become large enough to tap the food supplies of the vine on a considerable scale, it begins to form a flower-bud, which breaks through the bark. The bud swells until it is the size of a small cabbage (Fig. 43a^2). It is dull, dark purplish. Then it opens, and gives forth a foul odour which attracts flies.

The giant flower has five petal-like organs, and in the centre is a large basin-shaped cavity (Fig. 43a). In the cavity is a broad disc bearing slender projections on its upper surface (Fig. 43a^1). Under the edge of the disc are either stamens or stigmas; the flowers are either male or female, and (for seeds to be formed) pollen has to be carried from one to the other, presumably by flies. After pollination the fruit ripens as the flower rots and becomes a mass of soft decaying material. The seeds are very small, and their method of dispersal is unknown.

Rafflesia plants are only found in deeply shaded forest. In Malaya, they have been found at a good many places in Perak, Pahang, and Kelantan. The botanical name of the Malayan species is *Rafflesia Hasseltii*. The Malay name is Bunga Pakma.

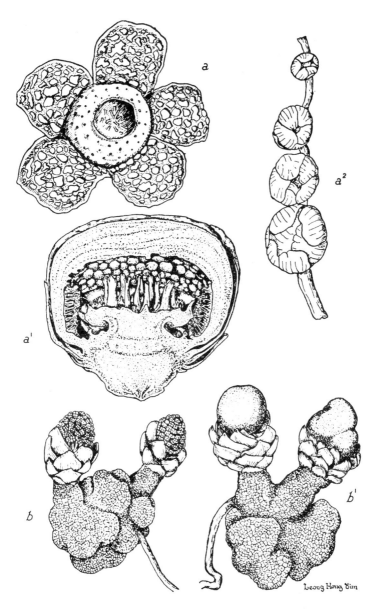

FIG 43—(a) *Rafflesia Hasseltii*: flower × $\frac{1}{5}$; (a^1) section of male flower bud × $\frac{2}{3}$; (a^2) unopened buds × $\frac{1}{5}$; (b) *Balanophora gigantea*: male plant; (b^1) female plant × $\frac{1}{3}$.

Such wonderful flowers must obviously have wonderful medicinal properties, and they are valued accordingly by people who have such ideas; but the value is probably quite imaginary.

Another genus of very strange parasites is called Balanophora. These plants live on the roots of trees in wet mountain forest. The commonest species is bright red, and at first sight one might take it for a fungus. But its club-shaped inflorescences have scale-leaves at the base, which distinguish them at once from a fungus, even when they are young and the flowers have not yet developed. The rhizome, which is attached by sucking organs to the host-root, is fleshy and warty but leafless. The flowers are unisexual (male and female on separate inflorescences) and the female flowers are very small (Fig. 43, b, b^1). The seeds also are very small, and their methods of dispersal and germination have not been studied. There is a less common brownish species, about which little is known, at Cameron Highlands. The genus Balanophora is widely distributed in the Indo-Malayan region, and also to Australia and to some islands in the Pacific.

The only other totally parasitic flowering plant in Malaya is Christisonia, which by contrast to Balanophora has very pretty flowers. It belongs to the Broom-rape family, of which a number of species are root-parasites in Europe. Christisonia grows on the roots of bamboos in primitive shady forest. The inflorescence is short-stalked and small; the flowers remind one of the pretty little Torenia often grown in our gardens. Christisonia seems to be a rare plant. The only place I have seen it is at Ulu Langat in Selangor.

The truly parasitic flowering plants are thus all forest plants, and except for Balanophora they are rare and local, so that few people ever see them. The partial parasites (or hemi-parasites), however, are very common, and they are also interesting biologically in many ways. In addition to the conspicuous mistletoes, there are small root-parasites of grasses which are common but inconspicuous.

When a mistletoe seed is deposited on a suitable tree branch, it begins to germinate, like any other seed, by development of its root. The root pierces through the bark of the tree, and enters the living tissue beneath, penetrating to the wood. It is thus able to absorb water from the water-stream in the tree. The mistletoe seedling then develops its first leaves, which are green, and so are able to manufacture food like other leaves. The young plant thus lives away from the ground, like an epiphyte, but it taps the tree's supply of water and salts, thereby solving the epiphyte's main problems of nutrition.

The mistletoe competes with the tree's own leaves for water. It may perhaps take other substances, but this has not been proved. What is certain is that the leaf-growth on the tree branch beyond the mistletoe plant is reduced, and the branch may eventually die. One can sometimes see an old tree so smothered with mistletoe that its own leaves can hardly be seen. Such a tree is near its end, and in such a case also the mistletoe will die from lack of water.

The commonest mistletoe in Singapore has a slight brownish fur on its young leaves; it is called Scurrula. Its root penetrates to the outer layer of the wood of its host, and then begins to grow around a circle at that level. Its absorption of water is not direct from the wood-vessels of the tree into its own wood-vessels, but through its living cells; the absorption is thus selective, as far as the dissolved substances are concerned. In other cases, it has been shown that the composition of the ash of a mistletoe may be very different from that of its host. As the Scurrula plant and its host-branch both grow, the wood of the host becomes gradually thicker, and then there is a zone of wood outside the Scurrula's first root; the Scurrula then grows another root round another (outer) circle inside the tree branch, and the same process is repeated later. In this way the Scurrula taps successive new zones of wood. Different kinds of mistletoe probably have differences in sucker development. The drawings in Fig. 44 show one of the other common kinds.

The Scurrula also attacks the tree in another way. As soon as it has produced a leafy branch, a small leafless branch grows from the base, close to the bark of the host-branch. This leafless branch of Scurrula creeps along the host-branch and at intervals puts down new roots or suckers into the wood of the host (Fig. 44a). Later it may produce a new leafy branch at any place where a sucker has developed, but in practice there are more suckers than leafy branches. The true Mistletoe of

Leong Hong Sim

FIG. 44—(a) *Viscum articulatum* × ½, with enlarged branch-tip; (b) *Dendrophthoe*, a common Malayan mistletoe: stem and flowers × ½; (b¹) mouth of flower × 2; (b²) creeping stem with suckers × ½; (b³) fruit × 1; (c) germination of seed of another kind of mistletoe (*Macrosolen*).

Europe, and also its near relatives in Malaya (one is common on old Waringin trees) have not this power of producing additional sucking organs.

The flowers of most of our Malayan mistletoes are tubular, not unlike Ixora flowers in general appearance, but really quite different in structure (Fig. 44, b^1). The four or five petals form a point at the tip of the unopened flower-bud; when ready, they are sensitive to touch and spring open when the flowers are visited by the small birds called flower-peckers. The stamens stand at the mouth of the tube, and shed their pollen on the bird as it sucks the nectar; the pollen will then be carried to another flower. The ovary of the flower is small, but very peculiar in structure; it produces one seed, which is surrounded by a sticky substance and outside this by sweet pulp.

The same little bird which ensured the production of a seed by its pollination may now come along and eat the fruit. It swallows the whole fruit (which is quite small) but digests only the sweet outer pulp. The seed is voided by the bird as it sits on a branch; the sticky covering of the seed is now exposed and ensures that the seed will remain attached to the branch while it germinates (Fig. 44c).

Some native Malayan mistletoes have beautiful bright red flowers, which you may find fallen to the forest floor if you take a walk at Fraser's Hill or Cameron Highlands. The lowland species are less beautiful, though there is a common one which has small red flowers. These Malayan members of the family differ a good deal from the true Mistletoe of Europe, which belongs to a different section of the family. But (as above noted) there are a few Malayan species which are quite nearly related to the true Mistletoe; they have very small flowers. One of them always grows on another mistletoe, not on a tree, thus taking its water-supply at second-hand. This hyper-parasite is a small jointed plant (Fig. 44a), apparently leafless; it is not uncommon in secondary jungle in some places in Singapore.

A very different parasite is often found on small trees near the sea, covering their branches with festoons of pale green, string-like, almost leafless stems (Fig. 45, a, a^1). This plant is called Cassytha, and strangely enough it belongs to the laurel family, most members of which are trees. The peculiar structure of the very small flowers, however, shows the relationship unmistakably. The stamens, nine in number, open by little flaps instead of the usual slits or pores (Fig. 45a^3). The habit of the plant is almost exactly like that of the Dodder, which grows on gorse and other plants in Britain. A Dodder is also sometimes seen in Malaya, but it is an introduced Chinese species, and it is confined at present to a few places only, near the main ports. As above noted, Cassytha stems are always very slender, and unable to support themselves. They climb by twining, and produce suckers at short intervals; the suckers have a dual function of supporting the Cassytha stem and of absorbing water. They probably absorb also some manufactured food, as the Cassytha stem is not very green even when young, and the leaves are minute; the old stems are hardly at all green.

Sometimes in open grassy places one may see a slender, erect, and almost leafless little plant a few inches tall, bearing pretty little yellow or pinkish flowers. This is called Striga, and it is parasitic on the roots of grasses (Fig. 45b). It belongs to the family Scrophulariaceae, and so is a relative of a number of other small root-parasites known in northern latitudes, namely the Eyebright, Lousewort, Yellow Rattle, etc. These European plants are more leafy than Striga, and presumably more independent of their hosts. It has been shown that Striga seeds will only germinate if they are in contact with water in which grass-roots have grown.

Turning now to saprophytic flowering plants, we find that most of them are orchids. The remarkable case of Galeola has already been mentioned (Chapter 10) and there are several other genera of saprophytic orchids, all of which live in very moist shady forest, nearly all being small and much less conspicuous than Galeola. They continue into adult life the dependence on fungi which all orchids experience as young seedlings. One interesting example may be recorded. A fairly large species of saprophytic orchid called *Epipogum roseum* is distributed from Africa to Australia, an unusually wide distribution in this family. The species, however, was never found in Malaya, in spite of much botanical collecting, until 1940, when it was found in a valley near Cameron Highlands.

There is another family in which the seeds are very small,

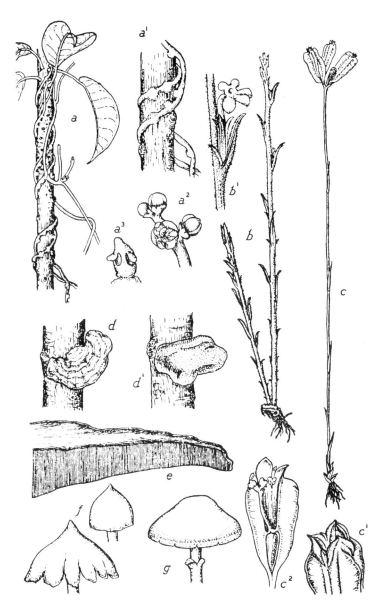

FIG. 45—(a) *Cassytha*: plant on *Excoecaria* branch × ½; (a¹) suckers × 1½;
(a²) inflorescence; (a³) a single stamen; (b) *Striga*: × 1; (b¹) flower enlarged;
(c) *Burmannia coelestis*: plant × 1; (c¹) mouth and (c²) section of flower; (d) a
small bracket fungus, from above, and (d¹) from below × ½; (e) section of a large
bracket fungus × ½; (f) termite toadstool, young and old × ½; (g) wild mushroom × ½.

for which reason it is often classed with the orchids, though the relationship between the two is doubtful. This family is called Burmanniaceae, and comprises two very interesting genera in Malaya. If you walk beside the MacRitchie Reservoir in Singapore, you will find here and there a little plant bearing a pale blue flower at the top of a very slender leafless stem (Fig. 45c). The stem is actually green, but the leaves are very small (all at the base), and it seems that the plant is partially saprophytic. Its delicate flower, though small, is quite complex in structure, with small, curiously reflexed stamens. A study of the germination of its minute seeds would be very interesting. This plant is called *Burmannia coelestis*.

In the forest are other kinds of Burmannia, some large with conspicuous leaves (fairly common in mountain forest), and some small with no leaves and no chlorophyll. There is an allied genus called Thismia, of which all species are small saprophytes; they live on the decaying leaves on the floor of moist shady forest, and are difficult to see though perhaps not rare. The flowers of Thismia are small, but elaborate and very strange in structure. An enlarged coloured drawing of a Thismia looks like a caricature of a flower. Probably nobody has ever cultivated a Thismia, though saprophytic orchids have been grown on artificial media for the purpose of studying their food requirements, and the relationship between orchid and fungus.

Now we come to the fungi, which are very numerous in Malaya. They are extremely important, and need not one book, but several, to themselves. Like Rafflesia, they have neither root nor stem nor leaves; but unlike Rafflesia they have no flowers. They are propagated by microscopic wind-borne spores.

When a fungus spore germinates, it produces a very slender thread. This thread has the power of digesting some substances outside itself; that is, it excretes a digestive juice which decomposes such substances and turns them into a simple soluble form which can diffuse into the living protoplasm of the fungus inside the thread. In this way the thread grows; it also branches, and forms a weft of threads which penetrate through decaying leaves and pieces of wood on the floor of the forest. When the weft of threads is large enough, it produces a fruit-body or fructification, on which new spores are borne, each of them capable of producing a new weft of threads. When we speak of fungi, we usually mean fructifications; but we must remember that there has to be a considerable mass of threads before the fructification can develop. The threads are called *hyphae*, and the weft is called a *mycelium*.

As above noted, fungi may be parasites or saprophytes. But some kinds of fungi may be either the one or the other, according to circumstances. A mycelium may live for a time in the dead branch of a tree, and then invade the living part of the tree, gradually killing it. Some fungi can live for a long time on decaying matter in the soil, and then attack the roots of particular kinds of plants when they appear. Some fungi, both saprophytes and parasites, are microscopically small; others are large, with fructifications weighing as much as a few pounds.

The toadstools which appear from time to time on the ground in forest are mostly saprophytes, but undoubtedly some of them, and perhaps a good many, live partly in association with the roots of trees, as mentioned below. Toadstools grow quickly and are soft and short-lived. Rain following dry weather is the stimulus to the development of their fructifications. Each particular kind of fungus takes its own time to respond. Some very small toadstools, which grow on dead leaves, are the first to appear. Afterwards each kind in its turn appears, not to reappear as fructifications until after the next change-of-season stimulus. Other fungi, such as those which cause decay of dead wood, may produce fructifications which take a considerable time to develop and which continue to grow and produce spores for a long period. Such fungi also grow more rapidly during wet weather, and fructifications will only start during such weather.

The association of a fungus with roots of trees or other plants is called *mycorrhiza* (meaning fungus-root). Such association takes different forms. One such we have already mentioned, namely the dependence of saprophytic flowering plants on fungi. These fungi, and the fungi which help young orchid seedlings, do not usually produce conspicuous fructifications. Indeed, the spores of some of them are unknown. Their service to the flowering plants with which they are associated is undoubted, though we do not know just how it works. Their hyphae penetrate the living cells of their associate, and are in turn deprived of their food-store by those cells. Clearly the fungus assimilates substances from the decaying humus of the forest floor and passes them on to its associated flowering partner. Clearly also the substances passed on include carbohydrates, the energy material which all plants need and which plants lacking chlorophyll cannot produce for themselves. The position of the fungi forming mycorrhiza in association with the roots of trees is quite another matter. It has been much studied in other countries in recent years, though not in Malaya, but is still not well understood. It is clear that in many cases the trees have some advantage from the association, but it seems probable that the trees also do something for the fungi, which saprophytic orchids hardly seem to do. In Europe, a large number of different fungi may form mycorrhiza on a single kind of tree, and this is probably true here also. The number of different kinds of trees in our forests is much greater than in Europe, but so also is the number of different kinds of fungi. Roots associated with fungi of this kind have rather thick much-branched young parts. The fungus forms a close mycelium completely surrounding the young root, the hyphae penetrating between the cells of the outer layers of the root. Probably the fungi actually take carbohydrates from the roots instead of passing them on as in the case of orchid seedlings. But it is also probable that the fungi absorb something from the humus of the forest which they pass on to the roots. How far the majority of forest trees are actually dependent on their fungus associates is not known, but certainly a few trees are quite dependent. Some years ago it was found that the Tenasserim pine would not grow in seed-beds at Cameron Highlands except when imported plants, infected with mycorrhiza, were grown in the same seed-beds. It may be that the Rhododendrons and other plants of the peat of our mountain ridges are also dependent in some way on mycorrhiza, as the heaths of northern latitudes are said to be (but this is still a disputed subject). So that the toadstools of our forests are perhaps after all not merely saprophytes, breaking down the decaying leaves and building up their substance again into living form; perhaps they are responsible for handing back an essential part of that material to the trees which shed the decaying leaves.

The larger fungi have two principal types of fructification; toadstool type and bracket type. Bracket-fungi are often, but not always, larger than toadstools, and vary much in size, some being quite massive, but the smallest are thin (Fig. 45d); in general, they have very numerous small pores in the lower surface (Fig. 45e), and the spores are produced by the cells which line these pores. A large bracket-fungus may sometimes produce spores in such quantities that they can be seen descending from it in a smoke-like cloud. In some cases many-pored types of fungi may be found forming a crust on the surface of old wood, not forming a bracket. Most of these Polypore fungi are wood-destroying, and most are saprophytes; but some may start as saprophytes in wounds of trees and then become parasites. In the latter class come some of the fungi which cause root diseases of Rubber trees. Wood-destroying fungi serve a useful purpose in natural forest, as they gradually decompose the substance of dead trees and so transform it that essential parts can be absorbed again by living plants.

Some fungi of toadstool shape are also Polypores; they are called Boletus. Probably most of them form mycorrhiza. Most toadstools, however, have the usual mushroom form, with thin gills radiating out from the top of the stalk, on the under surface of the cap. The spores of the fungus are produced by cells on the surfaces of the gills; the gills are always exactly vertical, so that the spores can fall freely when discharged.

A near relative of the cultivated mushroom is not uncommon in grass lawns in Malaya (Fig. 45g). It may be recognized by the following characters: there is a ring halfway down the stalk where the skin of the cap was earlier attached; the skin of the cap peels easily; the gills are at first pink and finally nearly black; the gills are quite free from the top of the stalk and do not run down it. This mushroom, like the forest toadstools already mentioned, appears when rain follows a dry period. Its fructifications are found for a few days only, and then one must wait until the next season. The mycelium of this fungus doubtless lives on the humus in the soil. That it has some effect on the grass may be seen by the "fairy rings" of darker green grass where the fungus occurs. These rings gradually increase in size and may later break up and form new rings.

Another kind of edible fungus is cultivated by termites. They plant it in their nests, and eat the mycelium, so that normally fructifications do not occur. When, however, part of the nest is abandoned, the mycelium grows strong enough to produce fructifications, which are well known to Malays as Chĕndawan Busut. They are excellent, but one must be very observant to secure them before they have been devoured by insects and other creatures; they are in any case short-lived. Termite toadstools have smooth grey caps, with a distinct central point, and white gills (Fig. 45*f*).

The true mushroom cultivated in temperate latitudes will not tolerate the lowland climate of Malaya; the maximum temperature which it will tolerate is about 70° F., which we experience rarely and that for an hour or two at early dawn. There is, however, another edible fungus, not a true mushroom, though having a gill-bearing cap; this is the rice-straw fungus or Canton mushroom and it will grow quite well in the lowlands of Malaya. It is especially grown in the rice country of the north. It can be eaten fresh, or dried and kept dry until needed. It is a species of Volvaria, with a cup-like structure at the base of the stalk; the cap is slimy to the touch.

Besides these larger fungi, there are innumerable smaller ones. Some consist of little but a mycelium, which proliferates as spores when it is strong enough. Such are the mould fungi which grow on our new shoes or other leather objects, or on stale bread. Some are parasites, causing death of young plants, or causing leaf-spots on old ones. Once such a parasite has attacked a plant, there is no cure except pruning and destroying the affected part, if that is possible. The only effective treatment is to prevent attack by the parasite, either by providing conditions (such as sun and air) not liked by the fungus, by applying a fungicide which will kill fungus spores before they can attack, or by growing kinds of plants which are not susceptible to attack. A large part of modern plant breeding is designed to produce such resistant plants.

CHAPTER FIFTEEN

WATER PLANTS

A WATER plant is a plant that lives in water; but that definition does not specify how much of the plant needs to be in water to qualify for the appellation. Apart from algae, there are very few plants that are totally submerged; and if once we admit plants which have some parts in the air and some in water, where are we to stop? Obviously, all mangrove and fresh-water swamp plants are water plants under such a definition. Here we will not adopt a hard and fast definition, but will deal with various plants which are at least rooted in water and not in dry land, and especially with such as are interesting from a biological standpoint.

A totally submerged plant is not in direct contact with the air. This has two main consequences as regards the life processes of the plant: oxygen and carbon dioxide can only be absorbed so far as these are dissolved in the water; and the normal transpiration stream of water from roots to leaves and then into the atmosphere cannot exist. The whole surface of such a plant is an absorbing organ both for dissolved gases and for dissolved salts. As gases are less soluble in warm water than in cooler water, such plants in the warm climate of Malaya will only flourish in shallow water, where the gases have not far to penetrate. In practice, however, the majority of the plants we shall here consider have part of their surface exposed to the air, if only by floating on the water surface.

If the roots and lower part of a plant are immersed in water (or in mud beneath water) and the rest of the plant is in air, these upper parts have access to the gases they need, namely oxygen for respiration and carbon dioxide for the building-up of carbohydrates. The roots also have plenty of water, and so there is no trouble about the transpiration stream. But the roots need oxygen for respiration just as much as the upper parts of the plant do. All living substances must continually respire, in order to obtain energy for essential life processes, and normal respiration means absorption of oxygen. The water surrounding the roots of water plants contains little oxygen, or perhaps in some cases none. The roots must use oxygen absorbed by the leaves or stems. Some oxygen so absorbed passes into the inter-cellular air spaces, which exist throughout the plant, and through these air spaces it diffuses to the roots. In normal plants, the air spaces are small, and the process of diffusion over such a distance would be too slow; therefore water plants have almost all developed a special system of large internal air channels, by means of which air from the upper parts of the plant readily reaches the roots. Such channels are easily seen in the stalk of a Lotus leaf.

An exception to this statement is shown by those plants which have special breathing roots. Such roots are able to take their own oxygen direct from the air. The commonest examples are shown by the mangrove trees called Avicennia or Api-Api and Sonneratia or Pĕrĕpat. These trees live at the seaward limit of mangrove, in mud which is only exposed for a rather short time at low tide. Their roots grow horizontally in the mud, and bear vertical branches which grow upwards a few inches above the level of the mud. These erect roots are aerating organs. When they are exposed to air, they can naturally absorb oxygen directly, but even when submerged, they are in moving water which is not deep and is fairly well aerated.

These roots serve also a second important purpose, which has only been pointed out in recent years. They bear small hori-zontal roots close to the surface of the mud (Fig. 46a). These are feeding roots, and as more mud is brought down by rivers, raising the surface level, new feeding roots can grow from the erect breathing roots. The latter thus ensure that feeding roots are always borne in the newest layer of mud, which is likely to contain the most nutrient material, and contains also more dissolved oxygen than deeper layers.

Other breathing roots are borne by Bruguiera trees (see Chap-ter 7) in the mangrove; these consist of more massive knee-shaped erect branches. They grow in the older parts of the mangrove where inundation is less prolonged and the soil surface more stable.

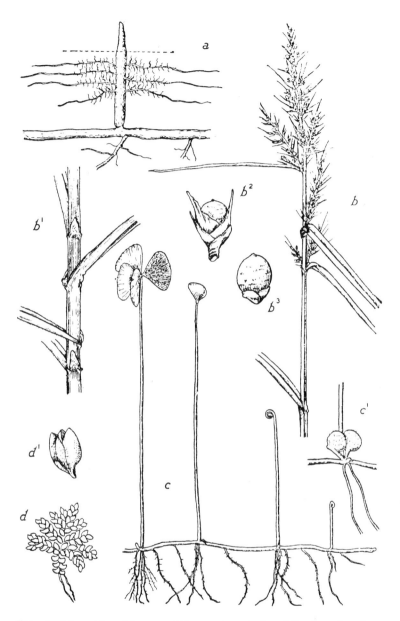

FIG. 46—(a) erect breathing root of *Sonneratia* × ¼; dotted line is mud-surface;
(b) *Scleria* × ½; (b¹) leaf-sheaths × ¾; (b²) fruit enclosed by bracts and (b³)
without bracts × 2; (c) *Marsilia:* rhizome and leaves × ½; (c¹) capsules × 2;
(d) *Azolla* × 1; (d¹) leaf enlarged.

In fresh-water swamp forest are other breathing roots of many kinds, especially in areas which are tidal. Some of these roots grow up and then down again, forming hoops which can trip one when walking in such forest. Others are massive, rather like those of the mangrove Bruguiera but larger; I have seen them almost as tall as myself, but such seem to be rare (at least in the Johore swamp forests). The common yellow-flowered bushes called Jussiaea, which grow in open swampy places, also have small aerating roots; these are spongy in texture.

The most important water plant in Malaya is, of course, Rice. Rice is a kind of grass; it is one of the short-lived grasses, and has a tufted habit. When it has flowered and fruited it dies, and new Rice has to be planted from seeds. Rice is interesting botanically because it has a peculiar spikelet, with a single floret containing six stamens; also because there are bristly auricles on each side of the base of the leaf-blade, much as in bamboos. There are two species of wild Rice in Malaya, and it may be that they are perennial, but no certain reports on this have been published. They need to be studied in cultivation. There are dry-land (or hill) varieties of Rice as well as wet Rice. Wet Rice is not entirely aquatic, as it needs water only during its growing period, the level being reduced to dryness at harvest.

There are many varieties of Rice in Malaya, and during the present century much work has been devoted to selecting those varieties best suited to particular localities as regards yield and other characteristics. The time of planting has to be adjusted so that harvest will coincide with the driest season. Varieties of Rice differ in the length of their life-period, some taking as much as seven to eight months, others much less. Some varieties will only flower if days are shortening; such are useless in the south of Malaya where day length is almost constant. If there is no artificial control of water-level, times of planting and harvest are entirely controlled by climate, and only one crop a year is possible. This is especially true in the north. In the south there is little rice (very little south of Malacca) and dry weather at harvest cannot be ensured. If water-supply can be suitably regulated, there is no reason why only one crop a year should be grown; but dry weather at harvest may not be assured.

When rice-fields lie fallow, a number of other aquatic or semi-aquatic plants grow in them, the chief being the various kinds of sedges; there are also a smaller number of aquatic grasses. Species of aquatic plants on the whole are more widely distributed than species of terrestrial plants, and a sign of this is the pantropic distribution of a number of our common sedges. Even in the grass family, many members of which also have a wide distribution, there are few species which are truly pantropic. Among the more peculiar of local sedges, the genus Scleria (which has more than a dozen species) may be mentioned (Fig. 46b). In most sedges the fruits are small and three-angled; they each contain one seed and so they are technically called nuts. The nuts of Scleria are in most cases almost spherical, and they grow so large that they are quite exposed. They are often white or nearly so, but in some species are bluish.

The sedges and grasses of fallow rice land are ploughed in before the Rice is replanted, to provide green manure. It has been shown in India that certain kinds of algae living in rice-fields have the power of fixing nitrogen and this may be an important factor in the economy of Rice cultivation.

A strange kind of fern called Marsilia is found in rice-fields in the north of Malaya. A Marsilia plant has a slender rhizome which grows in the mud and bears erect leaves (Fig. 46c), each of which has four equal leaflets arranged as in a four-leaved clover. When the water is fairly deep, the Marsilia plants are not very active. They produce rather few long-stalked leaves and the leaflets float on the surface of the water in a symmetrical cross-pattern. As the water level falls (the rice harvest approaching), Marsilia plants become more active, and then produce more but smaller and shorter leaves. Finally the plants are almost entirely exposed to air, at which time they bear their reproductive organs, in curious little capsules at the bases of the leaf-stalks (Fig. 46c[1]). These capsules contain sporangia of two kinds, containing large and small spores. The spores produce prothalli (see Chapter 11), but they are much reduced as compared with those of normal ferns; large spores produce female, small spores male prothalli, and after fertilization a new Marsilia plant is produced. But the old plants do not all die; those that survive produce their floating leaves again when the next flood-

P

ing of the rice-fields takes place. Thus the life of the Marsilia fern has a rhythm which is conditioned by the rise and fall of water in the rice-fields.

Two little floating ferns are often classified with Marsilia because they also have spores of two kinds, but they and Marsilia are probably not nearly related; like Marsilia they are not very fern-like in appearance. One of them is called Azolla (Fig. 46d). It commonly grows with duck-weed on the surface of fish-ponds. Its grey-green (sometimes reddish) colour and branching habit, with minute overlapping leaves and slender roots which hang in the water, are quite distinctive. It has an alga living in association with it, and the alga is said to fix nitrogen, for which reason Azolla is valued as a manure of rice land in Indo-China and carefully propagated from year to year. The other floating fern is a little larger, with leaves up to half an inch long; it is not common, and only found in the north.

Duck-weed is the name given to tiny floating green plants which are often abundant on the surface of ponds. In other countries they are eaten by ducks; here their chief use seems to be as food for fish. They are flowering plants of a very reduced kind; it seems that they rarely flower in Malaya. Most duck-weeds belong to the genus Lemna. Under favourable conditions the plants branch freely, branches becoming detached as new plants. Each branch has one or more roots hanging down into the water (Fig. 47, b, b^1). The plants float owing to the presence of internal air spaces. There is one minute duck-weed called Wolffia, much smaller than Lemna. It is the smallest of all flowering plants; each individual consists only of a very small, almost spherical green mass, without any roots. It grows with Lemna on ponds where the water contains suitable nutrients, and is encouraged by fish rearers as it is a valuable food for the young fry of carp, which are too small to take larger plants.

Along with the duck-weeds and Azolla, a floating plant with larger leaves is also fairly common. This is the Water Lettuce, *Pistia stratiotes* (Fig. 47a). It is called the Water Lettuce because each plant is shaped rather like a young lettuce, with a rosette of fresh green leaves; the roots hang freely in the water. Pistia commonly grows along with Water Hyacinth (see below) and with

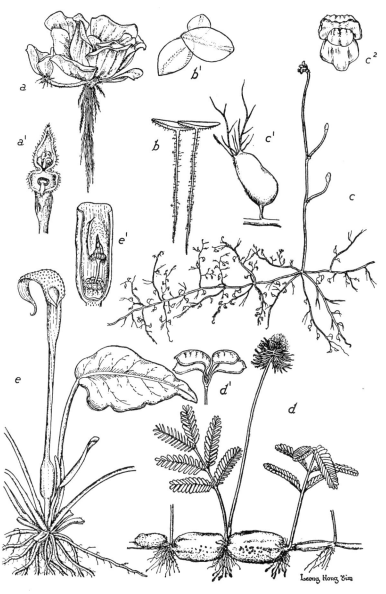

Fig. 47—(a) *Pistia* × ½; (a¹) inflorescence × 2; (b) *Lemna* from side, and (b¹) from above, × 2; (c) *Utricularia* × 1; (c¹) bladder × 10; (c²) flower × 2; (d) *Neptunia;* (d¹) fruits × ½; (e) *Cryptocoryne Griffithii* × ½; (e¹) base of spathe cut open to show flowers.

it is eaten by pigs, but it is much less bulky than the Water Hyacinth and would not seem to be an important pig food. Pistia belongs to the Arum family, but the flowers are small and inconspicuous. In each inflorescence is a single male flower and a single female one (Fig. 47a[1]).

The Water Hyacinth also can grow as a floating plant, and for this it is adapted by the swollen bladder-like bases of its leaf-stalks, but in shallow water it roots in the mud and grows much faster under such conditions, unless the concentration of plant nutrients in the water is maintained by regular additions (as in the case of Chinese ponds in Singapore). The botanical name of the Water Hyacinth is *Eichhornia crassipes*. It was introduced to tropical Asia from its home in the American tropics before the year 1900 as an ornamental plant, because of its beautiful lilac flowers (which, however, are very short-lived). It soon proved to be a troublesome weed of rice-fields and waterways on account of its prolific growth and rapid propagation by breaking up of old plants. It is now proscribed as a weed in most countries in tropical Asia, but in Singapore, where it is not a pest, its cultivation as pig food continues. A pond full of Eichhornia in full flower is a very beautiful sight. Eichhornia is a monocotyledon, and belongs to a small family allied to the Lily family.

Another floating plant of quite a different character is *Neptunia oleracea* (Fig. 47d). This is a near relative of the Sensitive plant (*Mimosa pudica*), but it has prostrate floating stems. The stems float by producing a mass of white spongy tissue, with many air spaces between the cells; this tissue is much greater in bulk than the rest of the stem. The leaves are sensitive in exactly the same way as those of the Sensitive plant. The flowers are small and yellow, in heads on slender erect stalks which rise a few inches above the water. The roots of Neptunia, like those of other floating plants, trail in the water.

We now come to a curious plant which has totally submerged leaves, but erect inflorescences which rise above the water; there are no roots, and water absorption (and absorption of dissolved substances) is carried out by the finely divided leaves (Fig. 47c). The plant floats because of its internal air spaces. The leaves bear very numerous small bladders; for this reason the plant is called Utricularia or Bladder-wort. It is common in rice-fields and other stagnant or slowly flowing water. There are two species of Utricularia which have this habit, one larger than the other, but they agree in essentials of structure.

The function of the bladders is to catch small animals and so provide additional food for the plant. The mechanism by which the bladders catch small animals is very intricate, and has only been fully investigated in recent years. Each bladder has an entrance closed by a small door which can open and shut, its edges normally resting against a framework which it fits exactly. The bladder is not spherical, but is flattened, with convex sides. When undisturbed, the cells of the wall of the bladder behave in such a way that water passes through them from inside to outside, so that the convex sides of the bladder gradually become concave, and the internal pressure is reduced. If the door is now disturbed, it is pushed inwards by the water pressure outside, and enough water is sucked in to equalize the pressure. The disturbing of the door can be done by touching certain hairs which surround the mouth of the bladder and so act as triggers (Fig. 47c^1). If a small organism touches a trigger, it will be swept into the bladder with the inrush of water in a fraction of a second. The trapped organism decomposes inside the bladder, and its substance is gradually absorbed by the plant. Meanwhile the door shuts and the trap is gradually reset by reduction of internal pressure.

There are other species of Utricularia which do not have floating leaves. Two of these, one with white flowers and one yellow, are common in shallow water round the reservoirs in Singapore, and in similar places elsewhere in Malaya. The plants appear to be rooted in mud, but the roots bear a few bladders like those on the leaves of floating species; whether these bladder-bearing organs should be called roots or leaves is not certain. There is one very remarkable species of Utricularia which grows in wet bog-moss on Kedah Peak; the stem of this is a slender twiner.

The most spectacular water plants in Malaya are the Lotus and the various species and cultivated varieties of Water-lilies. The Lotus is useful as well as beautiful; its seeds and its rhizome are edible, but these products are mainly imported, and in Malaya the Lotus is chiefly cultivated for its flowers. The flowers are picked when their petals are about full-grown, but have not begun to expand; their tips are then carefully pulled back, displaying their colour, but in an entirely artificial way. The reason is that the fully opened flowers are too fragile and too short-lived to be useful for sale as cut flowers.

Some people confuse a Lotus and a Water-lily, but the distinction between the two is very clear, whatever part of the plant may be available. The Lotus has a long creeping rhizome (runner) in the mud, and from it puts up a succession of well-spaced leaves and flowers in a row; the Water-lily has a short stout rhizome that bears a rosette of several leaves and flowers all together from its tip. The Lotus has leaves which are umbrella-shaped, with stalk attached in the middle; Water-lily leaves have not this shape. Lotus leaves (except on young plants) rise on tall stalks high above the water; Water-lily leaves always float on the water. Lotus flowers rise as high as the leaves on tall stalks; they have a most strange inverted cone in the middle, which contains the fruits (usually called seeds) embedded in its upper surface. Water-lily flowers grow on short stalks close to the surface of the water, and lack this inverted cone in the centre; they have an ovary of many chambers shaped (in horizontal section) like sectors of a circle, each containing many ovules.

The Lotus is native all across the warmer parts of Asia. The normal form of the plant (which alone is wild) has pink flowers. A cultivated variety with white flowers is often grown in Malaya; it appears that further north other varieties are grown. In North America is a beautiful pale-yellow Lotus, growing in the same way as ours, but in cooler latitudes. The two species have been hybridized at Honolulu, and the result is a series of apricot shades which have not yet appeared in Malaya. Lotus plants need sun; they are not part of the native forest vegetation of Malaya, and were probably brought by man.

True Water-lilies grow in ditches in various parts of Malaya, but the wild ones are inferior in size and variety of colouring to the cultivated ones, some of which are the result of the crossing of African species in America. There are two ways in which Water-lily flowers react to temperature. The white, pink, and red hybrids of the African *Nymphaea lotus*, which are the commonest cultivated Water-lilies here, open their flowers at night, and close them as soon as the sun is hot; the same flower will open on a few successive days. The blue Water-lilies have a contrary behaviour; they open their flowers as soon as the sun is hot, and close them towards evening. Like the Lotus, all Water-lilies need full sun. In the shade of the forest are a few native Malayan members of the Water-lily family, but their flowers are small.

Water plants are grown in aquaria because they absorb the carbon dioxide given off by fish in respiration, and replenish the oxygen in the water; in short, the plants and fish balance each other in their needs. If an aquarium is kept indoors, the plants do not have a very strong light; plants which are native in shaded Malayan forest streams are therefore suited for this purpose. One genus of such plants, called Cryptocoryne, has beautiful slightly variegated and totally submerged leaves; species of this genus, some native in our forests, are known to people who keep aquaria in all parts of the world (Fig. 47e). These plants only produce above-water parts in connection with their flowering. They have an inflorescence very like that of the white "Arum Lily". The leafy part, or spathe, rises above the water, and the spike bearing the many small flowers grows inside it (Fig. 47e¹). The base of the spathe forms a funnel, open to the air, and so the flowers are in air, not water (though below water-level), but the fruits later ripen under water.

There is a larger Cryptocoryne, which grows in open places in brackish water. It has taller leaves, which rise above the water, but the flowers are similarly produced below water-level, and the fruits ripen under water. When they are ripe, they break open, and liberate the seeds, which float to the water surface, and are carried about by tidal currents and so dispersed.

Besides these flowering plants, there is a fairly common fern, which grows in ditches, ponds, and other open water. This fern has leaves rather like those of a carrot; it is called Ceratopteris (Fig. 48a). In some countries Ceratopteris is an annual plant, dying with the drying of the waters each year and growing again from spores (the spores are large, and will germinate either under water or on mud exposed to the air). Nobody has studied the behaviour of Ceratopteris in Malaya. Perhaps its behaviour varies according to local variation in climatic conditions.

In fresh water also are green plants called Algae, which are important as foods for small aquatic animals. Some of them consist of delicate filaments, and the mass of these forms a sort of green scum. Others consist of single isolated cells. There is also one much larger green Alga called Chara, which has a fairly stout stem and whorls of slender branches which are branched again, giving a formal habit. Chara is interesting because its large cells show streaming of protoplasm in a remarkable way; this can be seen by moderate magnification with the microscope.

There are other Algae in the sea, but most of them are brown or red, not green. They are the familiar seaweeds. But in the sea also are lesser-known plants which have flowers. One of these is of great interest, and is locally common on muddy shores in Malaya, in places where it is exposed at low tide. It is called Enhalus (Fig. 48b). The leaves of the plant are rather like those of the Spider-lily in form; that is, they are strap-shaped and some eighteen inches or more long. The flowers are of two kinds, borne on separate plants, male and female. The male flowers are produced in short compact inflorescences covered when young by two hairy sheaths (Fig. 48b¹). When these flowers are ready to open, they become detached and rise to the surface of the water, where they open while floating and expose their stamens (Fig. 48b³). The female flowers are much larger, each at the end of a fairly long stalk. They open on a rising tide, and are kept on the surface of the water by their petals, which spread and float like the leaves of a Water-lily; the stigma is thus carried erect just above at the surface of the water. A freely floating male flower may now drift along and pollinate the stigma. The stalk of the female flower now contracts in a spiral, and the fruit ripens under water (Fig. 48b²). Flowering of these plants follows exposure at unusually low tides; the drying acts as a stimulus.

The largest seaweeds are found in cooler seas than those of Malaya, but in suitable places, on rocky coasts and on coral reefs, seaweeds are quite abundant on our coasts, and some of them are useful. More of them might be so if there were more convenient ways of procuring them in quantity.

Fig. 48—(a) *Ceratopteris* × 1, with (a¹) part of fertile leaflet enlarged; (b) *Enhalus Koenigii*: plant with ripening fruit × ½; (b¹) male inflorescence × ½; (b²) fruit × ½; (b³) male flower × 4; (c) *Sargassum* × ½; (c¹) shows fertile branches.

The largest of the brown seaweeds are called Sargassum; there are several species. The plants are up to two yards or more long, and consist of tough, slender branching stems bearing leaf-like organs and also bladders (looking like little fruits) on separate short branches (Fig. 48c). The bladders ensure that the leafy parts float upwards with the rising tide, thus keeping near the aerated surface water. The plants have much the same habit as flowering plants, but they are very different in internal structure and in method of reproduction. They are related to the Bladder-wrack or Fucus of cooler seas. Their reproductive organs are produced in small cavities in short slender branches (Fig. 48c[1]). They produce large egg-cells and very small motile male cells, as in a fern; but both kinds of reproductive cells are discharged into the sea (into rock pools at low tide), where fertilization occurs. I have searched for these reproductive cells in Sargassum in Singapore, but have rarely found them; perhaps they are only produced after exceptionally low tides, or after some other change in the environment of the plants.

Sargassum could produce the same useful substances as the larger seaweeds of northern seas; the principal such substance is alginic acid, obtained from the gelatinous cell-walls of brown Algae. The various salts of alginic acid have many technical uses, in food, textile, and other industries.

The Algae which are at present most used in Malaya are those known by the Malay name Agar-agar. These are red Algae, but some of them are very faintly coloured. They are boiled with water and then (in domestic use) strained through a fine cloth. A gelatinous substance passes through the cloth, leaving an unusable solid residue. Such agar-agar jelly can be obtained from several different red Algae, the product varying slightly. On the commercial scale, extraction methods involving freezing are used, and the gelatinous product is dried for sale. Before the war, Japan had almost a world monopoly of agar-agar production. When the war cut off this supply from other countries, production elsewhere (notably in New Zealand) was stimulated. As with alginates, agar-agar has many technical uses.

CHAPTER SIXTEEN

PLANTS AND ANTS

A NTS are a familiar part of life in Malaya. There are many kinds, and they are found everywhere; the field botanist meets them at every turn. The most troublesome are the large red Kĕrĕnggas, which make their nests by sticking the leaves of trees together, and are very aggressive when disturbed. They seem to be especially fond of some kinds of trees (e.g. the tree Bauhinias), and it might be possible to make some interesting observations on their preferences, but I know of no such having been put on record. The object of the present chapter is to call attention to ways in which ants are associated with particular kinds of plants, and particularly the cases in which plants give shelter to ants in some way. The ants also do something for the plants in some cases, but the advantage to the plant is often not obvious. An account of the Pitcher-plants, which probably catch more ants than any other kind of insects, is also included here. (Note: termites are often called white ants, but they are a totally different group of insects, and are not referred to in this chapter.)

Besides Kĕrĕnggas, which climb on plants in order to make their nests, other kinds of ants are commonly found on plants in search of food. This food is provided in some cases by nectaries, both of flowers and also on certain young flower-stalks, leaves, and other parts of plants. Several kinds of orchids have nectaries on parts of the young inflorescence (flower-stalks and bracts). A common example is the ground orchid called Arundina (see Chapter 3). Ants are always found licking the sweet liquid from such nectaries. But a more important source of food from plants is obtained at second-hand. The sucking insects called scales, mealy bugs, and aphids (or green flies) suck more sugars than they need from the plants, and exude excess sugars and other substances. These are taken by ants. This is the reason why scales or mealy bugs are always associated with ants. In some cases the ants actually carry young sucking insects, place them on young parts of plants, and then "milk" them when they are established. In natural forest, such sucking insects are rarely abundant, as they are controlled by parasites and other enemies, but on cultivated plants the balance of nature is upset and sucking insects are sometimes abundant and troublesome.

Ants also obtain food from the seeds of some plants. In a number of cases of small-seeded plants, there is a special part of the seed which contains fat, which the ants particularly need in their food. The ants carry off the seeds to their nests because of this, and a proportion of the seeds germinate there. In this way the seeds of the plant are dispersed, and also find a suitable place to germinate; and the resulting plants also help to shelter the ants. Besides seeds, similar food is also found in the sporangia of some ferns, and these ferns are also associated with ants' nests.

The genus Dischidia consists of some twenty-five species in Malaya, and several of them are associated with ants. They are epiphytes with rather slender creeping stems, which cling to the bark of trees by their roots, and rather small fleshy leaves. The flowers are also small, though complex in structure, and are followed by slender fruits which contain small plumed seeds. The seeds are thus wind-dispersed, but they are seized by ants when they finally fall to the ground and taken to a place where they can germinate. The service the plants do for the ants is to provide shelters with their leaves, in various ways.

The most remarkable species of Dischidia is called *Dischidia Rafflesiana* (Fig. 49a). It was named by Wallich, who found it first in Singapore, where he came at Raffles' invitation soon after the foundation of the settlement. This species is still fairly common in Singapore on bare dying branches of old trees in quite exposed places, often near the sea. It has two kinds of leaves. One kind are small and round, less than an inch in diameter. The other kind are much larger, and hollow, commonly about three inches long, ellipsoid in shape. If you split one of these leaves, you will find inside a mass of branching white roots, which belong to the plant itself; they creep into the leaf to

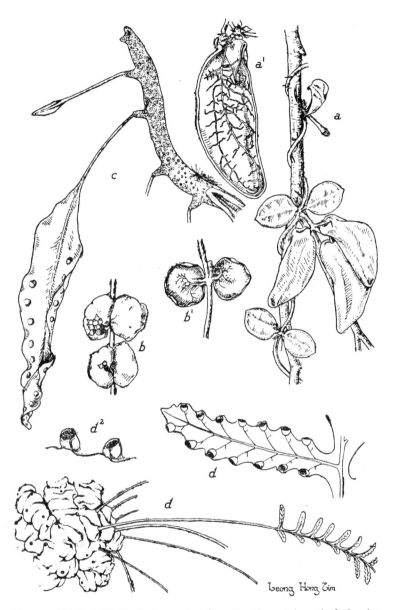

FIG. 49—(a) *Dischidia Rafflesiana* × ½; (a¹) section through large leaf, showing roots within × ¾; (b) a *Dischidia* with round convex leaves, upper surface and (b¹) lower surface × ½; (c) *Polypodium sinuosum* × ½; (d) *Lecanopteris:* ant-inhabited stem with bases of leaves × ⅓; (d¹) one leaflet × 1; (d²) part of edge with two sori × 2.

hide from the hot sun and dry air (Fig. 49a[1]). Inside the pitcher leaves, besides roots, are nearly always found some ants, which make their home there. The ants bring some earth to the roots, and also doubtless provide nitrogenous matter with their excreta. But they are not wholly beneficial to the plant, as they bring (or at least tend) scale insects which attack the inside surface of the leaves in some cases.

Some other kinds of Dischidia have all leaves alike, in shape about midway between the two kinds of *Dischidia Rafflesiana*. The leaves are almost hemispherical and hollow, the convex side outwards and the edges in close contact with the bark of the tree (Fig. 49b). The roots grow under the shelter of the leaves, and ants also make nests there. The commonest of these Dischidias has little red flowers and is called *Dischidia coccinea*; it is found both in lowland and mountain forest.

There are other Dischidias with leaves not convex. These are also associated with ants, the earthy nests of which give them rooting place, and presumably the roots help to hold the ants' nest together. The commonest such species is called *Dischidia Gaudichaudii*; it is very abundant on the trunks and branches of old trees, bearing small very fleshy leaves and pretty little flowers (Fig. 15a). As already noted, the seeds of these plants provide some food for the ants.

Another and quite different case of parts of leaves forming a shelter for ants is shown by the genus of Rotans called Korthalsia (see Chapter 13). Here the sheath of the leaf is extended upwards round the stem above the point of insertion of the leaf-stalk (Fig. 50a). This extension of the sheath is swollen and hollow, and is often inhabited by ants. There is no obvious advantage to the plant, and the presence of ants seems less constant. Some kinds of ants will use almost any kind of shelter for nesting purposes. Thus they use the hollow of the spathes of the other Rotan, Daemonorops. These spathes are stiff erect sheaths that cover the inflorescences; they are not shed until the fruits are ripe, but gape open just enough to expose the flowers, which are in a dense branched panicle (Fig. 42g).

There are a number of quite different plants which have hollow stems in which ants make their nests. The internal cavities are formed naturally by the plant, and are taken advantage of by

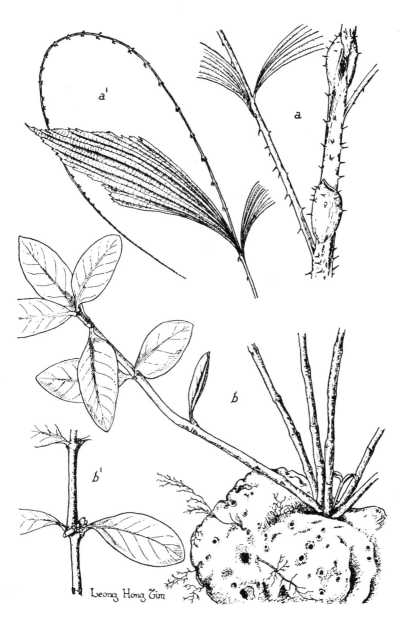

FIG. 50—(*a*) stem of *Korthalsia*, showing inflated ocrea at top of each leaf-sheath × ½; (*a*¹) tip of leaf bearing thorns × ½; (*b*) *Hydnophytum:* swollen base of plant showing roots and ant-holes, with bases of leafy stems; (*b*¹) flower-buds and two young fruits × ½.

the ants. In some of these cases the ants are said to protect the plant from attack by other insects (caterpillars), but this is difficult to prove. In some cases certainly the ants disperse the seeds of the plants because of the presence of fat in part of the seed. The kinds of plants which give shelter to ants in this way may be divided into three groups: ferns, epiphytic flowering plants, and trees.

Three kinds of Malayan ferns have thick fleshy but hollow rhizomes, and ants live in the rhizomes. Two are common species, one in the lowlands, one in mountain forest; the third seems to be a much less common lowland plant.

Polypodium sinuosum is often found growing on the same tree branches as *Dischidia Rafflesiana*. It has a rather flat rhizome about one centimetre wide, covered with small overlapping, nearly round scales, giving it a rather snake-like aspect; the rhizome bears short-stalked simple fronds which (when fertile) have a row of fairly large naked round sori on each side of the midrib (Fig. 49c). The rhizome is hollow, and almost invariably full of ants. The hollow is formed by the collapse of large thin-walled cells in the interior. As with other ant-inhabited ferns, the sporangia have a fat-body and are thus carried off by ants as food. Each leaf is jointed to the rhizome, and when old falls, leaving a small stump with a neat scar at the top. The old parts of the rhizome persist for some time, and the ants remain in them until they decay.

The less common lowland fern is called *Polypodium crustaceum*; it has very similar scales all over its rhizome, but the rhizome is much more massive than that of *Polypodium sinuosum*. The rhizome branches freely, the branches lying close together and forming a crust on the surface of a tree branch; there are swellings on the rhizome, each bearing a frond, which again is jointed at the base. The fronds are much larger than those of *Polypodium sinuosum* and deeply lobed (almost pinnate), the lobes narrow, each with two rows of sori arranged as on the simple frond of *Polypodium sinuosum*. I have seen this fern on trees on the edge of primitive forest by the Sedili river, Johore. It used to grow on the upper branches of tall trees on Bukit Timah, Singapore, but I have seen no sign of it there in recent years, nor have I anywhere seen old pieces of rhizome on the ground in forest, as one commonly sees pieces of the Lecanopteris next to be described.

Lecanopteris carnosa is one of the most remarkable and one of the commonest ferns of mountain forest in Malaya (Fig. 49, *d*, *d*[1]). Its crustose branching rhizome literally covers almost all the branches of the crowns of many forest trees; it is invariably inhabited by countless ants, so that the trees in question are living ants' nests. The curious thing about the rhizome of this fern is that it is quite smooth, totally lacking any protective scales. The young parts are green, and the old parts, which are very persistent, almost black. The fern goes on growing towards the tips of the tree branches, the old parts gradually dying and very slowly rotting, so that odd pieces fall to the ground from time to time, when they look more like a fungus than a fern. These fallen pieces of old rhizome show the swellings which each bear a frond, and the scars of fallen fronds. The fronds themselves are pinnate, the sporangia in little cups along the edges of the leaflets; the cups are curiously reflexed.

The ants which inhabit the rhizome of Lecanopteris bring small seeds to their nest, and some of these seeds grow in the crevices between the branches of the fern-rhizome, rooting beneath it on the bark of the tree and doubtless in some measure supplied with mineral matter by the ants. Among the plants which thus grow on the old parts of Lecanopteris are certain small orchids. These orchids in their turn help to make shelter for other plants. Eventually the branch of the tree, which originally only bore Lecanopteris, becomes burdened with a great mass of epiphytes.

The epiphytic flowering plants which have ants living in their hollowed stem are called Hydnophytum and Myrmecodia. The former is probably the more abundant. They are especially found on old Mangrove trees and on trees near the sea and by rivers. In both cases the basal part of the stem becomes swollen into a large tuberous fleshy structure, in which are branched tunnels; the ants live in these tunnels, which have openings made by them on the outside of the stem. In Hydnophytum, the swollen stem is smooth (Fig. 50*b*), in Myrmecodia it is prickly. Both plants belong to the family Rubiaceae (Ixora family) and

Q

have opposite leaves; they have quite small white flowers. The flowers of Myrmecodia arise from depressions in the stem. The fruits of these plants are soft and fleshy, and the seeds in them are distributed by ants. The seeds can germinate without rest, and the first thing a seedling does is to begin to form the tuber by a swelling of the axis below the cotyledons (i.e. of the hypocotyl). The tuber acts as a store of water for the plant, enabling it to grow in exposed places. As in the case of other epiphytes, the ants' chief help to the plants is probably the provision of minerals for their roots.

Our third group of ant-inhabited plants are very different from the ferns and other epiphytes; they are common trees of bělukar (secondary forest) belonging to the genus Macaranga, known by the Malay name Mahang (Fig. 51a). There are more than twenty native species of the genus, and several are common. Eight harbour ants, three of these being especially common.

The internodes of the young stems, a little way behind the growing tip, become slightly swollen, and the pith in them disintegrates, so that they are hollow. Ants now make little holes in the stems, and enter the hollow pith, making their nests in it. They also bring into the nest young scale insects, which suck the tissues of the stem from within and supply food to the ants. The trees also provide other food directly to the ants in the form of "food-bodies" which are white granules produced on the under side of stipules or young leaves (Fig. 51a[1]). These food-bodies are taken and given to the young ants inside the stem. I have never yet cut a stem of one of these Macarangas without finding ants in it. Ridley stated that he had seen young plants that were not ant-inhabited, and they had their leaves eaten by caterpillars, and he considered that the ants protected the tree from such enemies. Certainly one does not find caterpillars on the ant-inhabited trees.

We will conclude this chapter by considering the pitcher-plants, which turn the tables very thoroughly on insects, especially ants, by snaring, drowning, and then digesting them. There is no question here who has the advantage.

Nepenthes plants are climbers of open country. They have stiff wiry stems which normally do not reach any great thickness, though they may climb up to twenty feet or so on small trees.

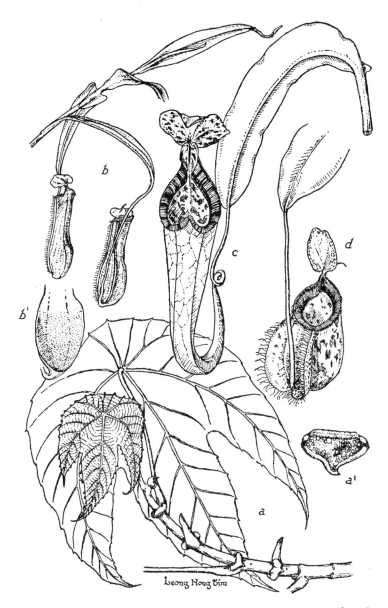

Leong Houg Tim

FIG. 51—(a) *Macaranga triloba:* stem with leaves and stipules × ½; (a¹) under surface of stipule showing food-bodies and ant × 2; (b) *Nepenthes gracilis:* tip of stem and two pitchers × ⅓; (b¹) base of pitcher cut open, showing glands × ⅔; (c) *Nepenthes Rafflesiana:* leaf and pitcher of climbing stem × ⅓; (d) *Nepenthes Rafflesiana* × *ampullaria* (hybrid): ground pitcher × ⅓.

Normally they start life in low scrub, where they scramble over the other plants, and persist only in the early stages of regeneration of forest. In Singapore they are characteristic of the scrub which develops very slowly on bare ground, especially where the soil is compacted and poor. They are not normally found in the primitive high forest that formerly covered most of Malaya, but they do occur on exposed mountain ridges, where again the washed-out soil is poor and will not support large trees.

Thus in Malaya our Nepenthes are divided rather sharply into two groups: one group of species which occur in the lowlands, the other of species which live only on mountains and do not flourish when brought to the warmer temperatures of the lowlands. Because the mountain species cannot spread away from their high ridges (prevented both by the forest around them and by the warm temperature of the neighbouring lowlands) they are as isolated as if the mountains were islands. Only a few thousand years ago (very recently in geological reckoning) Malaya, Borneo, and Sumatra were all joined together, and where now is sea between them was then lowland forest, with open places on river banks, etc., where the lowland Nepenthes could live; but the mountain species were just as isolated then as they are now. The result has been that on the isolated mountain masses of Sumatra, Malaya, and Borneo, isolated Nepenthes populations have evolved independently and have produced distinctive species. The common Nepenthes of our mountains does not occur in Sumatra or Borneo, but the common lowland species occur throughout all three countries.

Nepenthes climb by means of tendrils produced by prolongations of the tips of the rather narrow leaves. On some leaves the tendrils are prolonged into pitchers, but not all of them. But pitchers are produced by almost all the leaves of young plants, the stems of which grow very slowly in length. A young plant thus has a rosette of leaves spreading on all sides of the short stem, and each leaf normally bears a pitcher on its slender tip; the bases of the pitchers are round, and rest on the ground. Only when the stem has produced leaves of full size does it begin to grow rapidly in length. The pitchers borne by climbing stems do not rest on the ground, and they differ from the ground pitchers by having slender curved bases which widen gradually. Thus one plant produces pitchers of two different kinds.

But all pitchers of a single species of Nepenthes agree in the shape of the rim of the pitcher and of the lid; characters of leaf-shape are also constant. It is these characters, therefore, that one must examine if one wishes to identify a Nepenthes plant. Besides differences in shape of pitchers growing under different conditions, there are also differences in colour among pitchers of the same species. Colour differences are probably in part influenced by environment and in part heritable; plants of the same species with distinctly different colour characters would be ranked as varieties by botanists. Novices are sometimes more impressed by colour than by shape, and so fail to realize the distinctive characters of a Nepenthes plant. Colour differences in Nepenthes have been little studied, and their inheritance is not understood; a study of this matter would be of considerable interest.

A pitcher of Nepenthes consists of body, rim, and lid. The body has liquid in it. The liquid is produced by the plant and consists of water containing a digestive ferment (or enzyme). The lower part of the inner surface of the pitcher bears numerous glands (Fig. 51b[1]) which produce the enzyme (the whole inner surface of *Nepenthes ampullaria* bears them). The inner surface of the pitcher above the glandular part is waxy and slippery, affording no foothold for an insect which falls into the liquid and tries to escape.

The rim or *peristome* of the pitcher is more or less funnel-shaped; it has a hard smooth ribbed surface and usually fine teeth on the lower or inner edge; along this edge also are glands which attract insects to the mouth of the pitcher. The shape of the peristome and the character of its ribbing are distinctive of each species of Nepenthes. The lid closes the pitcher when it is young; when the pitcher is fully developed the lid usually stands horizontally above the mouth and so prevents heavy rain from entering. There are often glands in the lid, visited by insects.

The pitchers thus have lures (the glands on lid and peristome) which attract insects. An insect easily slips on the peristome and falls into the liquid, where it is drowned. Its body is then gradually digested by the enzyme, and the simpler decomposition-products, brought into solution, are absorbed by the walls of the pitcher. In this way the Nepenthes plant absorbs nitrogenous material and whatever other substances the bodies of insects afford. This material enables Nepenthes plants to live in very poor soil where otherwise they could not flourish.

In the lowlands of Malaya the commonest species of Nepenthes are *Nepenthes ampullaria*, *Nepenthes gracilis*, and *Nepenthes Rafflesiana*. On Penang Hill a pretty little species called *Nepenthes albomarginata*, with a white ring just below the peristome, is common. On our higher mountains the common species is *Nepenthes sanguinea*.

Nepenthes ampullaria has rather stout rough purplish stems and unstalked leaves. The pitchers are only produced in groups on the ground, on young plants, or on short branches from the prostrate stems of old plants. In some areas of secondary forest in Singapore these groups of pitchers are very abundant. The peristome is broad and smooth, and the lid very narrow and reflexed, thus being useless to keep water out of the pitchers. The result is that after heavy rain the pitchers are full; another result is that the pitchers breed mosquito larvae freely, in spite of the presence of a digestive enzyme which would kill the larvae if it were in great enough concentration.

Nepenthes Rafflesiana has also stout stems, but the leaves are stalked, and climbing stems bear large pitchers (Fig. 51c). The peristome is fairly broad, toothed on its lower edge and carried upwards into a neck below the attachment of the round lid. This is a very fine species, with the largest pitchers of any lowland Nepenthes. There is a hybrid between *Nepenthes Rafflesiana* and *Nepenthes ampullaria*; the hybrid is closely intermediate between the two parent species in most characters (Fig. 51d). The lid is broadly elliptic (i.e. neither round nor very narrow) and it stands erect (neither horizontal over the mouth nor reflexed). This hybrid is fairly common in Singapore.

Nepenthes gracilis has much more slender stems, with narrower unstalked leaves which run down the sides of the stem a little (Fig. 51b). It has small narrowly cylindrical pitchers, a very narrow peristome, and a round lid. It is very common in Singapore, growing along with *Nepenthes ampullaria*, but the two rarely hybridize. The hybrid is, however, found occasionally; it is more like *Nepenthes gracilis* in general aspect, though showing the influence of the other species in most characters.

Nepenthes plants have rather dense inflorescences, of small flowers, at the ends of the stems from time to time. The flowers in an inflorescence are either male or female. Male flowers have four sepals, no petals, and the anthers are crowded at the top of a short columnar growth in the middle of the flower; there is no ovary. The female flowers are similar in sepals, but have an ovary and stigma instead of the group of stamens. The sepals in both kinds of flower are covered with small glands, which produce sweet nectar freely when the flowers are newly opened. This nectar probably attracts small insects which effects pollination, but I have rarely seen insects on such flowers; do they come at night? Normally all female flowers produce fruits containing abundant seeds, so that pollination on a considerable scale certainly occurs. The fruits are dry, elongate, and break open to liberate their seeds. The seeds are like little bits of fibre, each with a small swelling in the middle. The swelling indicates the position of the embryo. The seeds are wind-dispersed. When a seed germinates, its first pair of leaves are the tiny cotyledons; soon the very first leaf after the cotyledons bears a very small pitcher.

CHAPTER SEVENTEEN

THE MALAYAN FOREST

IN the foregoing chapters we have considered various types of plants which live in Malaya, especially in relation to their adaptations to the climate and other environmental factors. We have frequently mentioned the Malayan forest, and the status of various kinds of plants in it. In this last chapter we will look at the forest as a whole, and at the interrelations of its parts. This chapter will, therefore, be in some measure a recapitulation, and an attempt at a synthesis, of part of the material discussed in the rest of the book.

Most readers of this book will perhaps live in towns, or near towns. The plants around such readers will not be forest plants, but mainly cultivated plants or weeds, or such local plants (a minority) as can exist outside the forest. To see the real Malaya one must go to primitive forest, and a visit to such forest (even if it be only to Bukit Timah in Singapore) brings one into a new world.

The structure of this forest is very complex. It consists of an enormous number of different kinds of plants, which are apparently arranged in a quite haphazard fashion. From this point of view, it may seem absurd to speak of the structure of the forest; confusion, not structure, seems to be the keynote. But yet all these varied plants are dependent on each other, they have definite relations to each other, and together they form a balanced organization.

The whole organization is controlled by the tallest trees; and only a limited number of kinds of trees have the power of attaining this controlling position. The crowns of these trees form a continuous canopy, interlocking with each other and casting shade on all other plants of the forest. The trunk of one of these trees is a hundred feet tall or more, straight and unbranched below the spreading crown. When such a tree is young, it has branches near the ground; but as it grows taller these branches cease growth owing to lack of light, and they are gradually shed, leaving no trace on the trunk of the fully grown tree. A large proportion of these tallest trees are members of the Dipterocarp family, but there are also members of several other families.

The lesser trees, ranging from large to small, are extremely varied. They all have this in common, that they have not the power of growing as tall as the biggest trees, and so must spend their lives in the shade of the crowns of such trees, except when the fall of a giant leaves a temporary gap in the canopy. The crowns of these lesser trees fit into each other and occupy a large part of the space below the top canopy; their successive layers of leafy branches cut off more and more of the light from the ground.

Among the trees are a certain number of tall monocotyledons (palms, bamboos, and pandans), but bamboos are most abundant where the trees have been partially felled by man; big palms are not common in primitive forest, and big pandans only flourish in fresh-water swamp-forest.

The lowest layers of plant-life, near the floor of the forest and in the deepest shade, are shrubs, small palms (e.g. the magic fan-palms called Licuala or Palas), gingers of many sizes (up to more than fifteen feet tall), ferns, and herbaceous plants; also young plants of all kinds, including tree seedlings at various stages of growth.

Besides all these plants, which stand on their own feet and are strong enough to support themselves, there are two other classes of plants which need the support of others. They are the climbers (Chapter 13) and the epiphytes (Chapters 10 and 11). The climbers are rooted in the ground, but use the trees to support them so that their leaves and flowers are carried upwards into the bright sunlight and free air. The epiphytes, needing a brighter light than the floor of the forest, have adapted themselves to perching on the branches of the trees. They thus occupy space otherwise not used, and in so doing have adapted themselves to the peculiar conditions of their habitat. Their most acute problem is water-supply, or the retention of sufficient water between rains; in this, epiphytes in some measure resemble desert plants. Hardly less important is their need of other substances, which they obtain by various means, calling in the help of fungi and ants.

Besides the climbers which reach the sun and outer air in the tallest tree-tops are lesser climbers, especially such as climb by means of roots, clinging to the trunks of trees, among them ferns and aroids; they rise as far as they can, having regard to the limitations of their internal water-conducting systems and to their toleration of dryness of air. Some only climb a few feet, others to a great height.

Similarly, there are epiphytes which cannot stand the exposure found in the crowns of the tallest trees, but lodge on the branches of lesser trees, or even of shrubs, or on their trunks, each kind adapting itself to a particular range of light and humidity of the air, each with its own methods of storing water and of withstanding excessive loss of water.

The ground plants have the most completely controlled environment, and therefore they are the least able to withstand change. Near ground level the air is almost still, because the countless leaves of the trees check the wind. Because the air is still, it is also moist; it is continually absorbing water-vapour from the soil, and only passes on this water-vapour slowly, by diffusion, to the upper levels; close to the ground the air is almost saturated a large part of the time in the most deeply shaded forest. The temperature of the air near the ground is also very constant. It is very little affected by the direct heat of the sun, and not subject to change through movement of the air.

The result is that near the ground the air is almost still, very humid, and very constant in temperature, and these conditions change very little throughout the year in most parts of Malaya. Our slight dry seasons will reduce the humidity near the ground for a time, but temperature is little affected. Measurements made some years ago on the ground in primitive forest in Selangor showed that the temperature did not vary more than $1°$ C. in three months. The intensity of light near the ground is usually less than one-hundredth of direct sunlight.

Plants living in such conditions will lose little water by evaporation, and they will have a weak light for use in photo-synthesis. They need, therefore, to spread their green matter as thinly as possible, to get the best effect from the available light; this means thin leaves, and it often means rather large leaves. Thin leaves also afford the maximum loss of water in proportion to bulk, and in very humid air this may be necessary if the plant is to absorb enough nutrient salts with its water. Some such plants exude excess water in mucilage. Plants adapted to these conditions are quite unable to stand the very different conditions of the open air and bright sunlight. If only some of the sheltering trees are removed, more sunlight reaches the ground, heating it and causing more rapid drying, and winds also help to dry the air; the thin leaves then lose more water than the roots can supply, and they therefore wither. If the change is made gradually, some such plants have a limited power of adaptation by development of tougher leaves, but in general the removal of part of the shade causes death of all the most sensitive of such plants.

Now we come to the roots of the plants, and the soil in which they live. The surface of the soil constantly receives the fallen leaves of all the plants of the forest. In our evergreen forest, there is no season of leaf-fall, but probably more leaves fall in the drier weather. (Except in the north, there is no prolonged dry season, and all our really primary forest is evergreen, though there may be some deciduous trees in it. Where such trees occur, they may all lose their leaves simultaneously and be bare for a short time; this will cause temporary drying of the interior air of the forest, and may stimulate some of the smaller plants to flower.)

The dead leaves on the ground are constantly moist, at least those which are in various stages of decay below the surface. These decaying leaves, and the black humus which they ultimately form, act as a sponge, absorbing much water from the rain and only passing it through slowly to the small forest streams. The decay of the dead leaves is largely brought about by fungi, some of which also live in association with the tree roots as mycorrhiza. As one digs down into the forest soil, one comes to the lower layers which are mainly formed of mineral matter, with little or no humus; depending on the nature of this subsoil, and on the nature of the roots, there will be more or less penetration of roots into it. The behaviour of the roots of our forest trees in Malaya has been little studied, but un-doubtedly a large proportion of them are in the upper layers of the soil, in contact with the decaying humus or with the soluble substances which are ultimately washed out of it to deeper levels.

The rotting leaves gradually make their substance available to the roots, and this substance, in the form of a dilute solution of simple chemical compounds, is carried upwards to the living leaves of the trees, where it is used to build up new organic material. The leaves in their turn die, and fall, and return their substance to the soil, where once more, by a process of decay, it is made available for the roots to absorb. Similarly, the fallen trunk of a forest tree slowly decays and returns its substance to the soil. So the plants of the forest keep on turning over their capital. The deep-going roots add to it by absorbing mineral substances from the lower levels of the soil, but there is a limit to the possibilities of this, and after a long period the forest reaches a balanced condition, the processes of decay and building-up matching each other. Within the forest there is also equili-brium in the dependence of all the other plants on the shade of the tallest trees, and the dependence of these tall trees also on the shelter and food given to their roots by all the other plants in the forest.

Among the plants in the lowest levels of the forest are seed-lings of all the tall trees, including the tallest. Though the crowns of these trees are exposed to the sun and wind, and are adapted to withstand such conditions, their seedlings can grow in the deep shade and moist air at ground level; if they could not, the forest could not regenerate itself. Some such seedlings are so adapted to such conditions that they will not grow in the open, or grow poorly under exposed conditions. In the forest shade they grow slowly; more slowly than most trees which will tolerate bright sunlight. They can only reach their full height when a break comes in the crown of the forest; when this happens, the strongest young tree available grows up and fills the gap.

Trees which grow only in strong light are usually sensitive to light, and show this by growing towards the strongest light. Such a tree, on the edge of the forest, will lean outwards. Many true forest trees do not behave in this way. No matter how the light around them is distributed, they grow vertically upwards. A striking example is the Kapur tree (*Dryobalanops aromatica*, a Dipterocarp, the tallest tree of our forest) which will tolerate almost full exposure when young. No matter where it is planted, it always grows perfectly erect. I think that seedlings of such forest trees are often more sensitive to the heat of the sun on their roots than on their leaves; if their roots are adequately shaded by other smaller plants, they will grow happily in the open and much faster than in the forest shade; but this is not true of all of them.

As we have already noted, many of the most sensitive of the shade-loving plants in the forest floor will die if some of the trees are cut down. If the whole of the forest is felled, a more drastic change takes place. The soil is exposed to the heat of the sun, to drying winds, and to full impact of heavy rain; it then rapidly decomposes or is washed away, and there is nothing to renew it. If at the same time the trees are burnt or removed, a large proportion of the capital of the forest, which had been slowly turning over and over for ages, is completely dissipated. If new plants begin to grow at once, and shelter the soil, much of it may be saved. But the new exposed conditions are unsuited to a majority of the forest plants. The ground is more or less quickly colonized by quite different, sun-loving plants, which on the whole grow more quickly than the forest plants.

The secondary forest or *bělukar* which appears where primitive forest has been cleared and the site abandoned, consists of trees the seedlings of which are light-demanding. They cannot grow in the shade of primitive forest, and are quite different from the trees of that forest. They are relatively short-lived. They establish a quick shade over the ground, and under their shelter seedlings of forest trees can again establish themselves, if the necessary seeds are present. That means, if there are forest trees near-by to supply the seeds. And so, after a period of many years, it may be possible for the original type of forest to be re-established. But in areas where there is wholesale felling of primary forest, the many species of plants which can only grow as part of such forest may be completely exterminated. This has occurred in the lowlands of Java; in that island there is no primitive forest at a lower elevation than 4,000 feet above sea-level, and many species have totally disappeared. Similarly, a large number of species of native plants have disappeared from the island of Singapore during the past fifty years.

If the ground on which primitive forest grew is used for cultivation of short-term crops which do not fully cover it, the humus rapidly disintegrates and is, of course, not renewed except by manuring. If later the ground is abandoned, its condition may have greatly deteriorated, and the secondary forest may take a much longer time to become established; it may also consist mainly of kinds of trees, shrubs, etc., which will tolerate extreme exposure, and it may thus differ from that bĕlukar which would have developed immediately after the primary forest had been felled.

The physical nature of the subsoil also has some effect on the kinds of plants which can develop. A light sandy soil, which dries quickly, gives very different conditions for the growth of roots from a heavy clay soil, which holds more moisture, dries more slowly, and also is less well aerated than sandy soil. The two soil types will thus develop different types of scrub and bĕlukar, but as the bĕlukar develops, and as dead leaves begin to accumulate and form humus, the difference between the growing conditions on the two soils will be reduced, and ultimately a similar forest may develop in the two cases. Extreme subsoil types, however, such as sand and limestone, usually develop peculiar types of primary forest, as these soils dry so quickly.

Another consequence of the felling of primary forest is the reduced water-holding capacity of the land. The layers of slowly decaying leaves of the floor of the forest act as a sponge, absorbing large quantities of rain-water and preventing sudden flow of this water into the streams. But if the sponge is destroyed by felling the forest, run-off of rain-water is far more rapid; erosion and flooding result after heavy rain.

Mountain forest differs from lowland forest in composition; there is an almost complete change, as regards species of all kinds, above about 4,000 feet, which is the upper limit of Dipterocarp forest. The tallest trees of mountain forest are often Oaks, of which there are many kinds; members of the

Laurel family also abound, and the mountain forest is often called Oak-laurel forest, but it contains also many other kinds of trees. The trees in this forest are not so tall as the Diptero-carps, and so the crown of the mountain forest is nearer the ground, and light on the ground is brighter. The ground vegeta-tion is therefore often more dense, and it includes a much larger number of pretty herbaceous flowering plants than low-land forest. But the ground vegetation of primitive forest in Malaya rarely forms a dense thicket, and there is always some bare ground surface; there are no plants like the grasses which may quickly form a continuous cover on bare ground in the open.

Another feature of mountain forest in many places is the frequency of mist or cloud, which provides abundant moisture for epiphytes. The result is that epiphytes are much more abundant in mountain forest, especially those that need very moist and shaded conditions, such as filmy ferns. The crowns of the trees being nearer the ground, high-level epiphytes are also more accessible and more evident to the traveller than in lowland forest, and they are also more abundant both in number of plants and in number of kinds. Mountain forest in Malaya is a botanist's paradise; the only places in lowland forest which can match it in variety and accessibility of plants are the edges of rivers, where bright light in the day and unusually moist air at night combine to make a very luxuriant epiphytic growth possible, almost down to river-level.

On the high mountain ridges, and near summits, the soil has through long ages become much washed-out, and so is poor in the mineral substances needed by plants. Such high ridges bear a smaller forest, or scrub, often much moss-laden; valley forest at the same elevation consists of much larger trees, and mosses do not dominate in the same way. This effect of poverty of soil will naturally be seen on isolated mountains at lower elevations than on the great mass of the Main Range. For example, the isolated Gunong Bĕlumut (3,300 feet) in the middle of Johore bears a quite dwarf mossy forest near its summit, whereas comparable forest at Cameron Highlands does not occur below about 6,000 feet. Among the plants of the higher mountain ridges are Rhododendrons of several species, which are very beautiful when in flower. With them pitcher plants are also common, and several kinds of ferns only grow in such places. Locally considerable quantities of bog moss (Sphagnum) may occur, forming a peat which is very acid. The upper part of Kedah Peak, where the poverty of the sandstone soil aids the effect of isolation, bears nothing but a dwarf forest in which Sphagnum is very abundant.

In some parts of Malaya, steep limestone hills are the dominant feature of the landscape. These hills bear a forest which is different from that of ordinary lowland forest, both in its trees and in the lesser plants. Some limestone plants are probably especially adapted to a soil containing much calcium, but others are merely adapted to dry conditions, such as cannot be found in normal lowland forest. Often such plants properly belong to the climatic region north of Malaya, or in some cases they are isolated species with their nearest relatives further north. Limestone rock soon becomes dry in a short dry season, and thus dry weather has a greater effect on plants growing on limestone than on more retentive soils. But some limestone plants are merely rock-plants, which will grow equally on other rocks; in Malaya, natural exposure of other kinds of rocks is rare.

There are two features of the Malayan forest, as regards its constituent species, which remain to be considered. One is the immense number of different species which are represented, and the other is the distribution of the individual species. Both of these groups of data have a bearing on the evolution and dispersal of plants in general.

In all parts of the world, the natural vegetation is adapted to the climatic conditions. Our high evergreen forest is a natural adaptation to the uniformly warm and wet Malayan climate, which permits the growth of plants at all times of the year. This forest has provided (as above indicated) a variety of different climates within itself and controlled by the tallest trees; plants have developed to suit the conditions of these various climates of the ground level, the middle heights, the branches of the crown, and the open sunlight. All these adaptations are due to evolution, which has occurred by natural selection of chance varieties over a long period of time (see Chapter 6). The variety of habitat has provided greater opportunities for variation than a uniform habitat could do.

This does not, however, explain why the Malayan forest consists of such a vast mixture of different kinds of trees, whereas forests in north temperate latitudes consist of few kinds. In Malaya, considerably more than two thousand species of forest trees exist, which is more than the total flora of all flowering plants in Britain. Probably part of the explanation is that the flora of Europe was impoverished by the Glacial Period, whereas the flora of Malaya has been evolving without such a disaster for a longer period of time. The continuous growing season of Malaya must also tend towards the more frequent production of variation, and it especially favours the growth of woody plants as against smaller ones. There are few parts of the world in which the flora is more varied.

One cause of restriction of distribution of individual species is the different temperature-range on mountains, and the adaptation of mountain species to that range, as distinct from the lowland range. The case of Nepenthes, in which the mountain species are quite distinct from the lowland ones, and distinct also from those of the mountains of Sumatra and Borneo, has been mentioned. This case can be matched by many others. Because mountain plants are adapted to a particular range of temperature, they cannot spread through the forest into the lowlands. The plants of an isolated mountain are thus in much the same position as the plants on an island. If they are to spread beyond the mountain, their seeds must in some way be carried to another mountain, over the top of the intervening lowland forest. This might obviously be done in some cases by wind or by birds, and no doubt it has been done. But some plants are not adapted to dispersal of seeds in this way. In any case, it is well known that isolation promotes the production of local varieties or species; the floras and faunas of oceanic islands are always different from those of the nearest mainlands. Similarly, on isolated mountains in tropical forest local species arise, and if their methods of seed dispersal are not suited to long-distance transport by air, they may remain isolated for a long time. Even a small mountain, if it has conditions on its summit which are distinctly different from conditions in the lowland forest round about, may develop a distinctive flora. There is little doubt that on the small mountain Gunong Panti

R

in south-east Johore, there are some peculiar species of flowering plants not found elsewhere in Malaya. In the genus Loxocarpus (belonging to Gesneraceae, the Gloxinia family) are three distinct species, one known on Gunong Panti, one on Gunong Bĕlumut, and a third on Mt. Ophir, all in Johore and all on isolated mountains. These small plants, and their relatives the Didymocarps which are so prolific on the Main Range, have very small seeds which are quite unsuited to aerial transport. And as they are produced near ground level in the forest they cannot normally be dispersed over any long distance.

Orchids, with their very small wind-borne seeds, are in a different position. There is evidence that a good many orchids of the mountains of Malaya are also found on the mountains of Sumatra. But it seems probable also that there are a good many mountain species peculiar to each land-mass. This is especially true of the terrestrial forest orchids, the seeds of which do not have much chance of being lifted out into the air above the trees; and perhaps in some cases they would not stand the consequent drying and exposure even if they were so lifted. In one genus of terrestrial mountain orchids (Hetaeria) there are three allied species, one on Mt. Ophir, one on Gunong Tahan, and one at Cameron Highlands; none of them has been found in Sumatra. Of course the proof is incomplete, but the data indicate probable localization of species.

It is especially terrestrial forest plants which are localized in this way because of the restrictions of their seed dispersal, and it is probable that in some cases even lowland forest species may be local in distribution. An example is given by the genus Scaphochlamys in the ginger family. At present twenty species of Scaphochlamys are recognized in Malaya; all are lowland forest plants, and all seem to be local in distribution. This contrasts with the allied genus Camptandra, in which the only lowland species is distributed throughout the forests of Malaya.

The distribution of individual species within Malaya and beyond its borders gives some very interesting data, which help us to understand the way evolution is occurring. But the information of this kind is still very imperfect; a lot of species are still known only from one collection, and we do not know for certain whether that means they do not occur at other places, or whether they just have not been noticed by collectors at other places. Though there is this kind of doubt in many cases, we do know enough to be able to make some generalizations, and can guess at others. But there is need for a much more intense botanical exploration, which will take many years, and it is more than likely that some species will be exterminated by clearing of forest before they are recorded.

BOTANICAL EQUIVALENTS OF
MALAY AND ENGLISH PLANT-NAMES

(This list is intended to guide readers who wish to obtain further information from other books on Malayan plants. Such books do not always agree as to the usage of some of the older botanical names, and alternatives are therefore given in such cases.)

African Marigold: Tagetes
African Tulip tree: Spathodea campanulata
African Violet: Saintpaulia ionantha
Akar: a root; also the woody stem of a climber
Akar Tuba: Derris elliptica
Angsana: Pterocarpus indicus
Api-Api: Avicennia
Avocado pear: Persea americana (or gratissima)
Bachang: Mangifera foetida
Bakau: Rhizophora
Banyan: Ficus bengalensis
Basong: Alstonia spathulata
Bira: Alocasia
Black Bryony: Tamus communis
Bladderwort: Utricularia
Bracken: Pteridium
Breadfruit: Artocarpus incisa (or communis or altilis)
Brinjal: Solanum melongena
Buah Susu: Passiflora laurifolia
Bungor: Lagerstroemia flos-reginae
Carpet grass: Axonopus affinis
Chengal: Balanocarpus Heimii
Chiku: Achras sapota
Dadap: Erythrina indica
Date palm: Phoenix dactylifera
Dodder: Cuscuta
Durian: Durio zibethinus

Egyptian Kidney bean: Dolichos lablab
Flame tree: Delonix (or Poinciana) regia
Gambier: Uncaria gambier
Gĕtah Gĕrip: Willughbeia
Gĕtah Gĕrip merah: Chonemorpha
Gĕtah Tĕrap: Artocarpus elastica
Giant bamboo: Dendrocalamus giganteus
Ginger (true): Zingiber officinale
Greater yam: Dioscorea alata
Guinea grass: Panicum maximum
Jack-fruit: Artocarpus heterophylla (or integrifolia)
Jagong: Zea mays
Jambu laut: Eugenia grandis
Jĕlutong: Dyera costulata
Jiring: Pithecellobium (or Pithecolobium) lobatum
Job's tears: Coix lachryma-jobi
Kabong: Arenga saccharifera (or pinnata)
Kachang Kara: Dolichos lablab
Kachang Parang: Canavalia ensiformis and C. gladiata
Kapur: Dryobalanops aromatica
Kĕmbang sa-mangkok: Scaphium affine
Kĕmpas: Koompassia malaccensis
Kĕmuning: Murraya paniculata (or exotica)
Keng Wah: Epiphyllum oxypetalum
Kĕladi: Colocasia
Kĕladi betawi: Xanthosoma
Kĕladi china: Colocasia antiquorum (or esculentum)
Lace fern: Nephrolepis exaltata, cultivated variety
Lalang: Imperata cylindrica
Languas: Languas (or Alpinia) galanga
Life-plant: Bryophyllum pinnatum (or calycinum)
Lotus: Nelumbo nucifera (or Nelumbium nelumbo)
Love grass: Chrysopogon aciculatus
Madder: Rubia tinctorum
Mahang: Macaranga
Malacca cane: Calamus scipionum
Mango: Mangifera indica
Mangosteen: Garcinia mangostana
Manila hemp: Musa textilis

Měngkuang: Pandanus atrocarpus
Měngkudu: Morinda
Měranti: Shorea
Midnight Horror: Oroxylum indicum
Mistletoe family: Loranthaceae
Nangka: Artocarpus heterophylla (or integrifolia)
Nest fern: Asplenium nidus
Nibong: Oncosperma tigillaria
Nipah: Nipa fruticans
Nutmeg: Myristica fragrans
Nyireh: Carapa
Oil palm: Elaeis guineensis
Pakma: Rafflesia
Palas: Licuala
Peepul: Ficus religiosa
Pěnaga: Mesua ferrea
Pepper: Piper nigrum
Pěrěpat: Sonneratia
Piai: Acrostichum
Pigeon orchid: Dendrobium crumenatum
Pinang: Areca catechu
Pineapple: Ananas comosus (or sativus)
Pitcher plants: Nepenthes
Pomelo: Citrus maxima (or grandis)
Pongpong: Cerbera
Potatoes, true: Solanum tuberosum
Potatoes, sweet: Ipomoea batatas
Pulai: Alstonia
Rambutan: Nephelium lappaceum
Rěsam: Gleichenia linearis
Rice: Oryza sativa
Rotan semambu: Calamus scipionum
Rubber tree: Hevea brasiliensis
Sago palm: Metroxylon sagus
Sělayar: Scaphium affine
Sěrangoon grass: Digitaria didactyla
Silk-cotton tree: Bombax (or Salmalia) malabaricum
Simpoh: Wormia suffruticosa
Sisal hemp: Agave sisalina

Stag's horn fern: Platycerium
Sugar-cane: Saccharum officinarum
Sword bean: Canavalia ensiformis
Tapioca: Manihot utilissima (or esculenta)
Tĕbu: Saccharum officinarum
Tĕmbusu: Fagraea fragrans
Tĕmu: Bruguiera
Tĕrong Pipit: Solanum torvum
Tomato: Lycopersicum esculentum
Ubi: Dioscorea alata and tubers in general
Ubi atas: Dioscorea bulbifera
Ubi kayu: Manihot utilissima (or esculenta)
Ubi kĕlĕdek: Ipomoea batatas
Waringin: Ficus benjamina
Water hyacinth: Eichhornia crassipes
Water lettuce: Pistia stratiotes
Water-lilies: Nymphaea
Yam: Dioscorea
Yautia: Xanthosoma

INDEX